D1274034

A Partridge in a Pear Tree

A PARTRIDGE IN A
PEAR TREE

A CELEBRATION FOR CHRISTMAS

ARRANGED BY

NEVILLE BRAYBROOKE

WITH DECORATIONS BY

BARBARA JONES

AND CHILDREN OF THE

HENRY FAWCETT SCHOOL

DARTON, LONGMAN & TODD
LONDON

Darton, Longman & Todd Ltd
29a Gloucester Road
London, SW7

Binding and endpaper designs by Barbara Jones
Text printed in Great Britain by The Faith Press Ltd., Leighton Buzzard
Typeface: 11 point Baskerville on 12 point body
Paper: Darenth offset cartridge and Jacobean art
Halftone four-colour blocks by The Arc Engraving Co. Ltd., London
Three-colour litho printing on binding by The Laburnam Printing Co.
Ltd., London

Line blocks for the text
Four-colour plates printed
Colour blocks for endpapers   } all by Messrs. W. & J. Mackay
Endpapers printed   & Co. Ltd., Chatham
Bound in Balacuir and blocked

CONTENTS

7

LIST OF ILLUSTRATIONS

'CHRIST'S cross me speed, and Saint Nicholas,' cries a shepherd in one of the early Wakefield pageants; and it is a line that telescopes the whole Christmas drama. For there cannot be birth without death, and Christ's nativity would have been meaningless without his passion. In the life of any religious hero, the sacrificial element is a factor that remains constant; it was apparent even in the old pagan celebrations held to mark the December solstice and return of the sun.

January the 6th was the original date set apart to mark the Saviour's birth, a date coinciding with the *epiphaneia*, or arrival of the wise men. Then in the middle of the Fourth century the feasts were separated—first in the Western, and next in the Eastern Church. The birthday was put back by thirteen days to the festival of the Unconquered Sun when (so report had it) Mithras the Sun God had leapt full-grown out of a rock, and when many centuries later (so the prophets had foretold) a child conceived of a virgin would be born in Judæa. In telling their stories after the event, the evangelists observed a strict economy of detail: Joseph's doubts about Mary's pregnancy are mentioned, and so is the angel that set his mind at rest; reference is made to Bethlehem, the arrival of the shepherds, and the wise men guided there by a star; and the fact that no room could be found in the inn is used to explain why the babe wrapped in swaddling clothes was laid in a manger. But the stable, ox and ass were all subsequent additions, since poets, painters and dramatists introduced them as a means of enriching their portraiture, and, with it, the experience of the whole human race. The elaborations which have stayed are those which have had *credibility,* if not *certainty,* on their side.

Likewise, in the Greek, the three travellers are wise men (μαγοι); they do not become kings until after the fifth century, although Tertullian speaks of his contemporaries regarding them 'almost as kings.' Later, Old Testament prophecies were called in to lend strength to events recorded in the New. Michael Fenwick, an Epiphany poet of this century, opens his poem with that passage from the Psalms beginning, 'the Kings of Tharsis and other islands shall offer gifts . . .', and it is not hard in the light of such texts to see how gradually the Magi became invested with the attributes of royalty. To poets such as Longfellow or W. B. Yeats the appeal was immediate. Yet legendary attributes do not spring from nowhere, and the legendary side of the Christmas story is continued in the undying life of the Christmas saint.

His sack is brimful from the centuries—with frankincense and French hens; with myrrh and turtle doves; with gold rings and swans carved in ivory; with silver partridges and peacocks from the kingdom of Tharsis; with colly birds from other islands and trees bursting with yellow pointed pears. And similarly the Saint Nicholas patronages grow: he is the intercessor of children, pipers, sailors, drummers, merchants and scholars, as well as of every kind of underdog. His bishop's cloak flies out in the wind and it becomes scarlet like a King's; the Dutch colonists sail to the New World with San Nicolaas, from whence spring the corruptions of Sint Klaus or Santa Claus; stockings hang beside bedsteads in Boston as once gifts were laid beside a manger; his team of reindeer are never far behind the camels that brought Melchior, Balthasar and Gaspar to the same scene. All add to the richness of the picture—whether a child's painting shows horses instead of dromedaries, or the Bethlehem cave be a tenement near the Oval. It would be a happy thought if his patronage which begins with children could be extended to all those others who have joined in this celebration.

For it is my hope that his spirit blows through these pages. I have chosen work by those of every and no belief, since every year towards the end of December there descends on earth a peace and good will toward men which no amount of commercialism or cheap vulgarity can destroy. Even in the trenches this spirit manifested itself—here described by Henry Williamson and David Jones—and their pieces make an interesting contrast with Robert Lowell's poem written about Christmas Eve during another world war. Indeed, contrast and continuity have been my chief guiding principles in selection. For this reason I open the anthology with a new translation into alliterative verse of an eighth century 'Dialogue Between Mary and Joseph'— possibly the earliest dramatic scene in English poetry—and follow it with Auden's 'Temptation of Saint Joseph,' with its beat reminiscent of a negro spiritual.

There are also new poems by Frances Bellerby, Charles Causley, Frances Cornford, Kevin Nichols, Meriol Trevor and Vernon Watkins; and new stories by Isobel English, L. P. Hartley, John Petty and Muriel Spark. Anna Green Winslow records an eighteenth century Christmas spent in New England when she was eleven, and Katherine Mansfield writes in her diary about a New Year she experienced in New Zealand when she was fourteen; Boswell's journal gives an account of London festivities in 1762, and Gertrude Bell recalls her stay in Bucharest during the winter of 1888; and written specially for this collection is Marion Agnew's moving description of a Christmas death in Rochester, New York, and L. Steni's recollections of an Edwardian Christmas outing which took place fifty years ago.

Editing such a book always brings its own rewards. 'Dickens the Dancer' was a piece I chanced upon quite unexpectedly in his house in Doughty Street, and an old issue of a Cornish magazine brought to light a charming 'Nöel' song by that beloved but most eccentric of clergymen, Sandys Wason. 'Robyns and Starres' comes from a rare emblem book, only once reprinted since 1633. Hardy's 'The Thieves Who Couldn't Help Sneezing' deserves to become better known since its first appearance during Queen Victoria's reign. Edward Thomas's 'Flowers of Frost' is salvaged from an early issue of *Country Life,* and Chesterton's festal poem to his fiancée was written on the fly-leaf of *The Wild Knight* six months before his marriage and comes from an unpublished album of his work.

'The spirit bloweth where it listeth.' That might be one way of explaining how this book was assembled. It might account for the inclusion of William Penn's mid-winter speech of peace to the American Red Indians in 1682, or Sir Frederick Treves' hospital memories of how, with the help of Mrs. Kendal 'the kindest of actresses,' it was made possible for a poor mis-shapen 'elephant man' to see a pantomime at Drury Lane. Such acts speak louder than words; they unite the centuries, bridge oceans and continents, and link surgeon and actress with Quaker and statesman. They are reminders of the true Christmas spirit. May they also prove an inspiration.   N.B.

The twelfth day of Christmas
My true love sent to me
Twelve lords a-leaping,
Eleven ladies dancing,
Ten pipers piping,
Nine drummers drumming,
Eight maids a-milking,
Seven swans a-swimming,
Six geese a-laying,
Five gold rings,
Four colly birds,
Three French hens,
Two turtle doves, and
A partridge in a pear tree.

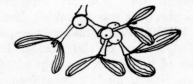

DIALOGUE BETWEEN MARY AND JOSEPH
—FROM THE ANGLO-SAXON

The Exeter Manuscript

Mary: 'O my Joseph,   son of Jacob,
          Kinsman of David,   the great King,
          Will you forsake   my firm affection,
          And leave my love?'

Joseph: 'I am sorely troubled
          Abased and humbled.   For you, I have heard
          Many a word   of measureless woe,
          Reproach and insult.   Men speak to me
          With scorn and derision   and rude disdain.
          In sadness of soul   I shed these tears.
          God can easily   heal my heart,
          And soothe the grief   of my troubled spirit.
          Alas, Maid Mary!   Maiden young!'

Mary: 'Why do you wail   and weep in sorrow?
          No fault in you   have I ever found,
          Nor any blemish   of evil done.
          And yet you speak   as if you yourself
          Were filled with evil   and every sin.'

Joseph: 'Much bane have I borne   by this conception.
          How can I silence   the hateful talk,
          Or find an answer   against my foes?
          It is widely known   that with happy heart
          I received from the shining Temple of God
          A spotless maiden   unstained of sin.
          Now all is altered,   I know not how.
          Speech or silence   avails me not:
          If I tell the truth   David's daughter must die,
          Stoned with stones.   Yet harder still
          If I shield the evil!   A man forsworn,
          I shall live hereafter   loathed in all lands,
          Despised among men.'

Mary: Then spoke the Maid;
        The Virgin revealed   the mystery:
        'By the Son of God,   the Saviour of Souls,
        I tell the truth,   I never have known
        The embraces of any man   ever on earth.
        As a girl in my home   to me it was granted
        That Heaven's High-Angel,   Gabriel,
        Gave me greeting   and said for truth
        The Heavenly Spirit   would shine upon me
        And I shall bring forth   the Flower of life,
        The radiant Splendour,   the exalted Son
        Of the King of Glory.   I am now become
        His Temple without taint.   The Comforter,
        The Holy Ghost   has home within me.
                Now put aside   this grief and sorrow;
        Say thanks eternal   unto God's great Son
        That, still a maid,   I am become His mother,
        And you His father called,   in wide belief,
        For prophecy   fulfils itself in Him.

                            Translated by CHARLES W. KENNEDY

THE TEMPTATION OF ST JOSEPH

Joseph: My shoes were shined, my pants were cleaned and
                pressed,
        And I was hurrying to meet
            My own true Love:
        But a great crowd grew and grew
        Till I could not push my way through,
            Because
        A star had fallen down the street;
            When they saw who I was,
        The police tried to do their best.

Chorus [*off*]:   *Joseph, you have heard*
                What Mary says occurred;
                Yes, it may be so.
                Is it likely? No.

Joseph: The bar was gay, the lighting well-designed,
        And I was sitting down to wait
            My own true Love:

16

A voice I'd heard before, I think,
Cried : 'This is on the House. I drink
  To him
Who does not know it is too late' ;
  When I asked for the time,
Everyone was very kind.

Chorus [off] :   Mary may be pure,
                      But, Joseph, are you sure?
                      How is one to tell?
                      Suppose, for instance . . . Well . . .

Joseph :   Through cracks, up ladders, into waters deep,
               I squeezed, I climbed, I swam to save
                 My own true Love :
               Under a dead apple tree
               I saw an ass ; when it saw me
                 It brayed ;
               A hermit sat in the mouth of a cave ;
                 When I asked him the way,
               He pretended to be asleep.

Chorus [off] :   Maybe, maybe not.
                      But, Joseph, you know what
                      Your world, of course, will say
                      About you anyway.

Joseph :   Where are you, Father, where?
               Caught in the jealous trap
               Of an empty house I hear
               As I sit alone in the dark
               Everything, everything,
               The drip of the bathroom tap,
               The creak of the sofa spring,
               The wind in the air-shaft, all
               Making the same remark
               Stupidly, stupidly,
               Over and over again.
               Father, what have I done?
               Answer me, Father, how
               Can I answer the tactless wall
               Or the pompous furniture now?
               Answer them . . .

Gabriel :   No, you must.

17

Joseph:	How then am I to know,
	Father, that you are just?
	Give me one reason.
Gabriel:	No.
Joseph:	All I ask is one
	Important and elegant proof
	That what my Love had done
	Was really at your will
	And that your will is Love.
Gabriel:	No, you must believe;
	Be silent, and sit still.

W. H. AUDEN, 1907–

THE FORESHADOWING

VIRGIL'S Fourth *Eclogue* was accepted and proclaimed as a direct prophecy of the birth of Christ. [*Sicelides Musae, paullo majora canamus,* or in Dryden's version:

Sicilian Muse, begin a loftier strain!
Though lowly shrubs, and trees that shade the Plain,
Delight not all; Sicilian Muse, prepare
To make the vocal Woods deserve a Consul's care.
The last great Age, foretold by sacred Rimes,
Renews its finish'd course: Saturnian times
Roll round again; and mighty years, begun
From their first Orb, in radiant circles run.
The base degenerate iron Offspring ends;
A golden Progeny from Heaven descends.
O chaste *Lucina!* speed the Mother's pains,
And haste the glorious Birth! thy own *Apollo* reigns!
The lovely Boy, with his auspicious face,
Shall *Pollio's* consulship and triumph grace.
Majestick months set out with him to their appointed Race.
The Father banish'd virtue shall restore,
And crimes shall threat the guilty World no more.
The Son shall lead the life of Gods, and be
By Gods and Heroes seen, and Gods and Heroes see.
The jarring Nations he in peace shall bind,
And with paternal Virtues rule Mankind.
Unbidden Earth shall wreathing Ivy bring
And fragrant Herbs (the promises of Spring)
As her first offerings to her infant King.]

Indeed, Virgil was thought of and treated as in some sense deified, and able from the other world to exercise control or intervention in human affairs. His birthday, like that of Augustus, was registered in the calendar as a saint's day. Poets, like Statius and Silius Italicus, worshipped at his tomb as at a shrine. Alexander Severus placed his bust in the *lararium* or family chapel of the Imperial palace, where divine honours were paid to it. This worship would have ceased with the decay of paganism; but it was taken over by the Christian Church. The Fourth *Eclogue* was expounded as a foreshadowing of Christ, in an address to the whole Christian population of the Empire, by Constantine after he had decreed the recognition of Christianity as the State religion. Thenceforth it was taken for granted, and almost became an article of faith. . . .

J. W. MACKAIL, 1859–1945

MANTUAN AND MESSIAH

VIRGIL's gods are grand or lovely or both, and it is possible to accept them in the imagination often poetically, and sometimes religiously. They are true to humanity, and, as the best pagan theologies will, they constitute a symbolic psychology. Jupiter, Venus and the Fate of Rome are together supreme, and worshipful almost as a trinity. But they are not the cause why Virgil was so soon thought a natural Christian at heart, *anima naturaliter Christiana*. Partly, it was an inevitable conclusion from the Fourth *Eclogue* and its almost Biblical imagery that Virgil foretold the birth of Christ. The truth of the matter seems to be that the Hebrew Bible and its thought were little known in Italy; but that the Sibylline oracles of the Greek east could have transmitted almost the same thought and imagery; and that Virgil, sensitive as few have been to the past and the present, chose the image of a baby to mark the golden age, as the early Christian generations themselves chose to contemplate not only the Christ of manhood, but also the Babe at Bethlehem. There was a necessity in it for both.

W. F. JACKSON KNIGHT, 1895–

BETHLEHEM

'Ecce, in hoc parvo terrae foramine caelorum con-
ditor natus est.'—Saint Paula, writing on the Cave of
the Nativity.

IT was early morning. I bowed my head to enter the low door-
way into the church of the Nativity. Inside, it was cool and
large and empty, like one of the great basilicas at Rome. There
is a royal splendour about this church built where a King was
born. In it, too, in 1101 a king was crowned: Baldwin I, who
refused to be crowned in Jerusalem, thinking it unfitting to be
thus honoured in a city where his Lord had worn a crown of
thorns. . . . Shafts of light coming through windows set high in
the walls broke upon faded mosaics and huge golden-red pillars.

At first I did not see the paintings on the pillars. Then one by
one mitres and halos took shape; crimson cloaks and purple
tunics, calm stylized faces, and a Virgin holding a Child.

Lamps hidden in striped cotton bags hung from the ceiling,
with a ball under each. The balls were large and bright: red and
blue, lime-green and gold and silver.

'How gaudy those balls look,' a woman's voice said at my
elbow. Her words rasped in the stillness of the church.

'I think they are charming,' I said crossly. 'Not at all in-
appropriate in a church that honours a child.'

. . .

On either side of the high altar a flight of worn rounded steps
led down into the cave where Christ was born. It was dark, and
yet full of light. Tapers were burning, and the glow of lamps
was reflected on a silver star nailed into the floor and bearing
upon it the words: *'Hic de Virgine Maria Jesus Christus natus
est.'* Above the star there was an altar, and in the nitch behind
it an ancient mosaic, damaged, yet still showing Mary in robes
of silver and blue and amethyst, and the face of the ox looking
towards the manger.

A few yards away, on the far side of the cave, three steps
between pillars—one red and strong, the other white and deli-
cately carved into a spiral—went down into the chapel of the
Manger. The Manger today is a rock-shelf overlaid with marble.
In the church of Constantine it had a covering of silver. Saint
Jerome regretted this. 'In honouring Christ,' he wrote, 'we have
taken away that clay manger and put in its place a silver one.
I prize more the one that has been taken away.'

I knelt on the pavement of the tiny chapel, while a Franciscan said Mass at the altar dedicated to the Magi. Across the cave the lamplight flickered on the silver star. There was no one but the priest and the server. No sound but the murmur of the Latin:

> *'Et ecce, stella, quam viderant in Oriente, antecedebat eos usque dum veniens staret supra ubi erat puer. Videntes autem stellam, gavisi sunt gaudio magno valde. Et intrantes domum invenerunt puerum cum Maria matre eius.'*

The star filled my thoughts. Was it, as some supposed, the conjunction of Jupiter and Saturn in the year 6 B.C.? Or the providential appearance of a comet? Or, as Saint Augustine said, was it a new star, unlike those that had observed their appointed course since the beginning of time, shining forth at the wonder of a virgin bearing a child? *'Novo partu virginis novum sidus apparuit.'* And was it seen by the Magi, as some held, two years before the birth of Christ? Or did it appear, as others believed, on the night he was born, and the Magi travelled in such hot haste that, whether by divine aid or by the speed of their camels, they completed their journey in thirteen days? . . . The silver star on the floor. The star that shone over Bethlehem. The Magi. The shepherds. The angels. The ox and the ass. Joseph. Mary. The Child. They were all gathered into the Mass that was being offered on the altar.

· · ·

A Franciscan brother was sweeping the floor in front of the altar of the Magi. A Greek monk was also sweeping near the place of the star. Close by an Armenian was filling a lamp. Much has been written about the squabbles at Bethlehem between the different churches. The Greeks, the Armenians, the Latins, have their allotted ground, their number of lamps, their rights and privileges. No one would pretend there have not been quarrels, some serious, none of them edifying. Yet, now, the atmosphere is more peaceful than for many years. A Franciscan told me a story that I like to remember. A Greek monk, hoping to extend the space allotted to his church, shifted his carpet a little further each day in the direction of the Latin altar. Seeing this, a Franciscan brought a pair of scissors and snipped off some inches of the offending carpet. I heard this story again from a Greek. This time the roles were reversed.

I went out of the cave by an underground passage that leads up to the church of Saint Catherine of Alexandria. It is tunnelled out of the natural rock, and off it are caverns that have been made into chapels. The first, which is dedicated to Saint Joseph, contains a painting on copper of the Saint being warned by an angel in a dream to flee with the child and his mother into Egypt. From here steps go down into the chapel of the Holy Innocents, those first martyrs whom Prudentius likened to rose-buds scattered by the wind:

> *Quos lucis ipso in limine*
> *Christi insecutor sustulit*
> *Ceu turbo nascentes rosas.*

Another of the chapels is said to be the cell in which Saint Jerome finished his translation of the Scriptures. In another is buried his pupil, Saint Eusebius of Cremona; in another Saint Paula, with her daughter, Eustochium. Saint Jerome wrote many letters to Paula, who was a Roman widow, descended from the family of the Scipios. She founded a convent at Bethlehem, as well as the monastery of which Saint Jerome was superior.

The winding, taperlit passage and the little rough-hewn cells, one opening into another, with their lights and pictures, were like a symbol of the overflowing of the Incarnation into the world beyond.

ELIZABETH HAMILTON, 1906–

ARTHUR MACHEN RECALLED

I SHOULD like to add one small remembrance of my own about Arthur Machen. On a certain December in the worst days of the last war, I made up my mind that this year, writing for a Sunday newspaper, there should be no Christmas article. What was the use, I thought, to speak of peace on earth, good-will to man, to people whose sons and husbands were lost, or prisoners of war, or far away from home; to wish good cheer to the bombed, the anxious and the lonely?

And then there came a letter from Arthur Machen in his

square, scholar's hand, recalling the story of the shipload of pilgrims who were due to get to Bethlehem on Christmas Eve. 'Suddenly a great storm arose and a clever man,' he wrote (and I still have the letter by me) 'who had somehow found his way aboard, said in a jeering fashion : "It will be a pity if we don't get there by Christmas Eve, won't it?" An old peasant with a white beard quietly replied, "It is always Christmas Eve at Bethlehem."'

C. A. LEJEUNE, 1897–

TRAVEL

Travel teaches toleration.

BENJAMIN DISRAELI, 1804–81

THE TWO CAVES

Cold, the cave was cold,
Underneath the world
Where the poor girl came
Far away from home.

No one noticed then
When she bore the man
Whom everyone would see
Nailed up on the tree.

Underneath the world
She would lay the child
Now within her hid,
In the tomb for dead.

But this golden king
Not held by any thing
Rises before the sun,
Turns the world upside down.

For she who carried him,
Girl and earth and time,
Was born out of his tomb,
By him was carried home.

MERIOL TREVOR, 1919–

23

THE Sicilian enjoyed representing the house of Nazareth, just as he enjoyed the legends which had grown up round it, and he easily fancied himself beside the Madonna as she rocked the cradle or washed the clothes or made the bread, while Saint Joseph worked from morn till eve teaching Gesuzzù to use the plane. Even when the Signuruzzù played, every bit of wood He fashioned took the shape of a cross, says one carol, unconsciously echoing the Apocryphal Gospels, and these legends and carols were repeated and sung in the Christmas Novena, varying in its customs all over the island. During the great period of crib-making the Christmas Novena was the most important time of the year, when the last touches were being given to the fine cribs of the artists and santibelli from the country.

It was also the moment for the Christmas marionette show, and nowhere had marionettes a stronger hold on popular favour than in Sicily, where their tradition went back to the days of Xenophon, while with the marionette plays came the serenades by shepherds who had come in from the hills. Two singers always went together, alternating the verses of their songs which they sang to the accompaniment of the fiddle or bagpipes. These serenades were intended as a 'devotion' to console the Mother of God for her sufferings in Bethlehem. They told of the shepherds approaching the manger laden with cheeses and a gourd full of milk, the old story of Bobi, Nencio, and Randello; then of the hunters carrying a little hare and a basket of chestnuts; after which came the carpenters with faggots to light the fire and dry the clothes, for who would go empty-handed to greet the Son of God? Then the singers, unconscious, no doubt, too, of the old canticle and plays which they were echoing, invited all good people to hasten also to Bethlehem by 'joining in this our humble prayer, for this is the night so long desired which is consecrated by the birth of the Eternal Word, who drives away the winter cold with the warmth of the joy He brings.'

These last words seem to take us back to very early Christian times, and the Sicilian shepherds with their bagpipes might be the prototypes of all the musician shepherds of the Presepio. These men seem to escape from time, and should one chance to hear them singing out on the hills, their voices follow cadences of immemorial age. It is so easy to imagine them in that still older world with pipe and syrinx playing and singing 'a pastoral melody' on the hills of Theocritus. NESTA DE ROBECK, 1886–

WAYE NOT HIS CRIBB . . .

Waye not His cribb, his wodden dishe,
  Nor beastes that by Him feede;
Way not His mother's poore attire,
  Nor Josephe's simple weede.

The stable is a Prince's courte,
  The cribb his chaire of State;
The beastes are parcell of His pompe,
  The wodden dishe His plate.

ROBERT SOUTHWELL, 1561–95

ST JOHN THE BAPTIST'S NATIVITY

WHOM can we conceive of such majestic and severe sanctity as
the Holy Baptist? He had a privilege which reached near upon
the prerogative of the Most Blessed Mother of God; for, if she
was conceived without sin, at least without sin he was born. She
was all-pure, all-holy, and sin had no part in her; but St John
was in the beginning of his existence a partaker of Adam's curse:
he lay under God's wrath, deprived of that grace which Adam
had received, and which is the life and strength of human nature.
Yet as soon as Christ, his Lord and Saviour, came to him, and
Mary saluted his own mother, Elizabeth, forthwith the grace of

25

God was given to him, and the original guilt was wiped away from his soul. And therefore it is that we celebrate the nativity of St John; nothing unholy does the Church celebrate; not St Peter's, nor St Paul's, nor St Augustine's, nor St Gregory's, nor St Bernard's, nor St Aloysius's, nor the nativity of any other Saint, however glorious, because they were all born in sin. She celebrates their conversions, their prerogatives, their martyrdoms, their deaths, their translations, but not their birth, because in no case was it holy. Three nativities alone does she commemorate, our Lord's, His Mother's, and, lastly, St John's. What a special gift was this, my brethren, separating the Baptist off, and distinguishing him from all prophets and preachers, who ever lived, however holy, except perhaps the prophet Jeremias! And such as was his commencement, was the course of his life. He was carried away by the Spirit into the desert, and there he lived on the simplest fare, in the rudest clothing, in the caves of wild beasts, apart from men, for thirty years, leading a life of mortification and of meditation, till he was called to preach penance, to proclaim the Christ, and to baptize Him; and then having done his work, and having left no act of sin on record, he was laid aside as an instrument which had lost its use, and languished in prison till he was suddenly cut off by the sword of the executioner. Sanctity is the one idea of him impressed upon us from first to last; a most marvellous Saint, a hermit from his childhood, then a preacher to a fallen people, and then a Martyr. Surely such a life fulfils the expectation which the salutation of Mary raised concerning him before his birth.

JOHN HENRY NEWMAN, 1801–90

WHO IS JESUS CHRIST?

IT is the fate of the most holy Mystery of the Incarnation to be misconceived by the world: 'the light shineth in the darkness, and the darkness comprehendeth it not.' But it is light for all that; and men, blind as they are, have their eyes, and, with God's help, can use them; and therefore it is reasonable to suppose that the best way to convince them of the existence of the Incarnation is to try and let them see what it is.

The thought of God is the great thought which takes hold of a man's mind and heart, and produces what is called Religion. The thought of God, revealed in the primitive revelation, has never quite died out of any corner of the earth. It is the reviving, the stirring up, the writing out at large of this thought of God, which has given the heathen from time to time grander and higher ideas of goodness and virtue. It is the proclamation from the heavens of this thought which men have called God's Revelation. And in the thought of God are included two thoughts. They are not so much two thoughts as two faces of the same thought; they differ from each other no otherwise than as the fiery mass of the sun is distinguished from the light that falls upon the world. God in His own nature—God in His contact with His creatures. The history of all religious thought—of natural religion, of revelation, of Judaism, heathenism, and Christianity, of orthodoxy, of heresy, of unbelief—it is all a history of the changes of men's thought as to what God is, and how He has come into communication with man. And the question, Who is Jesus Christ? cannot be answered without treating afresh the old thoughts.

J. C. HEDLEY, 1837–1915

JESU'S LYFELYNE

O F the offspringe of the gentleman Jafeth come Abraham, Moses, Aaron, and the Prophets, also the King of the right line of Mary, of whom that gentle-man Jesu was borne.

JULIANA BERNERS, *fl.* 1375

REVELATIONS OF DIVINE LOVE

H E brought our Lady Saint Mary to my understanding. I saw her ghostly, in bodily likeness: a simple maiden and a meek, young of age and little waxen above a child, in the stature as she was when she conceived. Also God shewed in part, the wisdom and the truth of her soul: wherein I understood the reverent beholding in which she beheld her God and maker, marvelling with great reverence that he would be born of her that was a simple creature of his making. And this wisdom and truth, knowing the greatness of her maker and the littleness of herself that was made, made her to say full meekly to Gabriel: *Lo me God's handmaiden!* In this sight I understood verily,

27

that she is more than all that God made beneath her in worthiness and grace; for above her is nothing that is made but the blessed manhood of Christ, as to my sight.

JULIAN OF NORWICH, 1342–1442

THE INCARNATION

For treuthe telleth that love is treacle to abate sinne
And most soveraine salve for soule and for body.
Love is a plante of peace, most precious of vertues,
For Hevene could not holde it, so heavie it seemed,
Till it had with earth alloyed itselfe.
Was never leafe upon linden lighter thereafter
As whenne it had of the folde flesh and blood taken.

WILLIAM LANGLAND, 1330–90

WOLCUM ALLE

Wolcum, Yol, thou mery man
In worchepe of this holy day!

Wolcum be thou, hevene king,
Wolcum, born in one morwening,
Wolcum, for hom we xal sing,
 Wolcum, Yol!

Wolcum be ye, Stefne and Jon,
Wolcum, Innocents everychon,
Wolcum, Thomas, marter one,
 Wolcum, Yol!

Wolcum be ye, Good Newe Yere,
Wolcum, Twelfthe Day, both in fere,
Wolcum, seintes lefe and dere,
 Wolcum, Yol!

Wolcum be ye, Candylmesse,
Wolcum be ye, qwyn of blyss,
Wolcum bothe to more and lesse,
    Wolcum, Yol!

Wolcum be ye that arn here,
Wolcum alle and mak good chere,
Wolcum alle another yere,
    Wolcum, Yol!

ANONYMOUS (Fifteenth Century)

TO MEN OF GOOD WILL

IN this work [of charitable contemplation] a perfect worker hath
no special beholding unto any man by himself, whether he be
kin or stranger, friend or foe. For all men him thinks equally
kin unto him, and no man stranger. All men him thinks be his
friends, and none his foes. Insomuch that him thinks all those
that pain him and do him dis-ease in this life, they be his full
and his special friends: and him thinketh that he is stirred to
will them as much good as he would to the homeliest friend that
he hath.

No man should be judged of other here in this life, for good
nor for evil that they do. Deeds may lawfully be judged . . . but
not the man.

The Cloud of Unknowing, ANONYMOUS (Fifteenth Century)

A PATTERNE OF COURTESIE

FOR ever, said Arthur, it is a worshipful knight's deed to help
another worshipful knight when he seeth him in a great danger;
for ever a worshipful man will be loath to see a worshipful
man shamed. And he that is of no worship, and fareth with
cowardice, never shall he show gentleness nor no manner of
goodness where he seeth a man in any danger, for then ever will
a coward show no mercy. And always a good man will do ever
to another man as he would be done to himself.

So then there were great feasts unto kings and dukes, and
revel, game, and play; and all manner of noblesse was used;
and he that was courteous true and faithful to his friend was that
time cherished . . .   SIR THOMAS MALORY, *fl.* 1470

A SPEECH TO THE AMERICAN RED INDIANS

ON a day towards the end of 1682 [we] made a Treaty of Amity with the American Red Indians. [We] carried no weapons; [they] were fully armed. [I] addressed them as follows: 'The Great Spirit who made me and you, who rules the heavens and earth, and knows the innermost thoughts of men, knows that I and my friends have a hearty desire to live in peace and friendship with you, and to serve you to the uttermost of our power. It is not our custom to use hostile weapons against our fellow-creatures, for which reason we have come unarmed. Our object is not to do injury, and thus provoke the Great Spirit, but to do good. We are met on the broad pathway of good faith and good will, so that no advantage is to be taken on either side, but all is to be openness, brotherhood, and love. I will not do as the Marylanders did, that is, call you children and brothers only; for often parents are apt to whip their children too severely, and brothers sometimes differ. Neither will I compare the friendship between us to a chain, for rains might sometimes rust it, or a tree might fall and break it. But I will consider you as Christians, of the same flesh and blood, and the same as if one man's body were to be divided into two parts.'

WILLIAM PENN, 1644–1718

CRADLE LULLABIE

Jesu, sweetë sonë, dear!
On poor-full bed liest thou here,
  And that me grieveth sore;
For thy cradle is as a bier,
Ox and assë be thy fere,
  Weep I may therefor.

Jesu, sweetë, be not wroth,
Though I have no clout nor cloth
  Thee on for to fold,

Thee on to fold, nor to wrap,
For I have neither clout nor lappe,
But lay thou thy feet to my pappe,
  And save thee from the cold.

ANONYMOUS (Fourteenth Century)

I SYNG OF A MAYDYN

I syng of a Maydyn
  That is makeles;
Kyng of alle kynges
  To her Sone she ches.

He cam al so stylle
  Where his moder was,
As dewe in Aprille
  That fallith on the gras.

He cam al so stylle
  To his moder's bowr,
As dewe in Aprille
  That fallith on the flour.

He cam al so stylle
  Where his moder lay,
As dewe in Aprille
  That fallith on the spray.

Moder and maydyn
  Was never non but she;
Wel may swych a lady
  Godes moder be.

ANONYMOUS (Fifteenth Century)

CHRIST, THE FLEUR-DE-LIS

For his love that bought us all dear
Listen, lordings, that be here
And I will tell you in fere

31

Where-of came the flower delice.
  Sing we all, for time it is,
  Mary hath borne the flower delice.

On Christmas night, when it was cold,
Our Lady lay among beasts bold,
And there she bare Jesu, Joseph told.
And thereof came the flower delice.
  Sing we all, for time it is,
  Mary hath borne the flower delice.

Of that beareth witness Saint John
That it was of much renown;
Baptized he was in flom Jordan,
And thereof came the flower delice.
  Sing we all, for time it is,
  Mary hath borne the flower delice.

On Good Friday the Child was slain
Beaten with scourges and all to-flayed,
That day he suffered much pain
And thereof came the flower delice.
  Sing we all, for time it is,
  Mary hath borne the flower delice.

     ANONYMOUS (Sixteenth Century)

THE SHIP CAROL

There comes a ship farr sailing then,
St Michael was the steersman,
St John sat in the horn;
Our Lord harped, our Lady sang,
And all the belles of heaven they rang,
On Christ's Sunday at morn.

     ANONYMOUS (Sixteenth Century)

THE HOLLIE AND THE IVY

The hollie and the ivy,
When they are both full growne,
Of all the trees that are in the wood,
The hollie bears the crowne:

The rising of the sun
And the running of the deer,
The playing of the merry organ,
Sweet singing in the choir.

The hollie bears a blossom,
As white as the lillie flower,
And Mary bore sweet Jesus Christ
To be our sweete Saviour:

The rising of the sun
And the running of the deer,
The playing of the merry organ,
Sweet singing in the choir.

The hollie bears a berrie,
As red as any blood,
And Mary bore sweet Jesus Christ
To do poor sinners good:

The rising of the sun
And the running of the deer,
The playing of the merry organ,
Sweet singing in the choir.

The hollie bears a prickle,
As sharp as any thorn,
And Mary bore sweet Jesus Christ
On Christmas Day in the morn:

The rising of the sun
And the running of the deer,
The playing of the merry organ,
Sweet singing in the choir.

C

The hollie bears a barke,
As bitter as any gall,
And Mary bore sweet Jesus Christ
For to redeem us alle :

The rising of the sun
And the running of the deer,
The playing of the merry organ,
Sweet singing in the choir.

The hollie and the ivy,
When they are both full growne,
Of all the trees that are in the wood,
The hollie bears the crowne :

The rising of the sun
And the running of the deer,
The playing of the merry organ,
Sweet singing in the choir.

ANONYMOUS (Sixteenth Century)

HARK! THE HERALD ANGELS SING

Hark! the herald angels sing,
Glory to the new-born King;
Peace on earth and mercy mild,
God and sinners reconciled!
Joyful all ye nations, rise,
Join the triumph of the skies;
With th' angelic host proclaim
Christ is born in Bethlehem.
Hark! the herald angels sing,
Glory to the new-born King.

Christ, by highest heav'n adored,
Christ, the everlasting Lord;
Late in time behold Him come,

Offspring of the Virgin's womb.
Veil'd in flesh the Godhead see,
Hail th' Incarnate Deity,
Pleased as Man with man to dwell,
Jesus, our Emmanuel!
Hark! the herald angels sing,
Glory to the new-born King.

Mild He lays His glory by,
Born that man no more may die;
Born to raise the sons of earth,
Born to give them second birth.
Ris'n with healing in His wings,
Light and life to all He brings,
Hail, the Son of Righteousness!
Hail, the heav'nborn Prince of Peace!
Hark! the herald angels sing,
Glory to the new-born King.

CHARLES WESLEY, 1763–91

A WORD ON CAROLS AND WAITS

THE carol was a dance before it became a song or a hymn. It was a measure danced by people in a ring, and so was the chorus. The choruses in old Greek tragedy were first of all the dancers who later on took to song. We keep that idea of chorus in the word choreographer for the man who arranges a ballet.

Then the dancing was forgotten and the chorus became the choir; the vocalist took over altogether. Choirs and carol-singers are not expected to do any leaping or pirouetting. 'Carol' itself is a beautiful word, and it has evoked some beautiful writing, but badly sung by scratchy voices in the street a carol can belie the charm of its name. 'Charm' itself is the Latin *carmen,* and began its life as a song, as in John Milton's 'The charm of earliest birds.'

We do not hear so much of the 'waits' now. They were a kind of town band. They did not dance or sing: they just blew; and they blew hardest of all at Christmas, passing the hat for reward. They were not always much liked. One of Ben Johnson's characters talks of the waits being pensioned not to come near his part

35

of the town; so 'Give them a shilling to play in the next street'
is an old piece of advice.

IVOR BROWN, 1891–

SACRED FLORA

THERE were several types of the Incarnation which were so
prominently employed in the divine offices from the earliest
times, that we should be surprised to find them absent in the
sacred flora of the Christmas season.

The prophecy of the dying Jacob which had sustained the
hope through the long ages of a coming of a Messias, was that
the sceptre and legislative power should not be utterly taken
away from the house of Judah until about the time when One
who was also the Expectation of the Gentiles should appear.
Again and again in the Advent offices the promise is re-echoed
*'Erit radix Jesse et Qui exurget regere gentes, in Eum gentes
sperabunt'* or *'Egredietur Virga de radice Jesse et Flos de radice
ejus ascendet; et requiescet super Eum Spiritus Domini.'* The
wail of one of the great O Antiphons continues the cry, *'O Radix
Jesse Qui stas in signum populorum veni liberandum nos, jam
noli tardare';* and finally at the Nativity the announcement is
heard: *'Germinavit Radix Jesse, orta est stella ex Jacob, Virgo
peperit Salvatorem.'*

In the similarity between the words *Virga*, a Rod, and *Virgo*,
the Virgin, the early symbolic writers found a fruitful source of
speculation. A Bishop of Chartres in 1007 composed the introit
for Mary's birthday which shews how they loved to play with
the words:

> *Stirps Jesse Virgam produxit, Virgoque Florem*
> *Et super hunc Florem requiescit Spiritus almus,*
> *Virgo Dei genitrix, Virga est; Flos, Filius ejus.*

It was from this simile that the luxuriantly designed Jesse-
trees arose with which most of us must be familiar in every form
of work of mediæval times, whether covering a plain surface
upon some domestic, civic, or ecclesiastical building, sculptured
in stone at the back of some altar, beautifully adapted to form
the tracery of a window; or brilliant with rich colouring in glass,
fresco, or embroidery. In every material and place it was one
of the artist's most lovely and useful designs, boundless in the

scope afforded for inventiveness and effectiveness, while redolent of the fundamental dogma of Christianity. The emblem was not even confined to decorative purposes but was applied to articles of furniture, and originated those many-branched brass candelabra once known as 'Jesse-trees,' now commonly called 'spiders,' but which were once common in churches and homes. They were especially frequent in Belgium and Germany, being invariably surmounted by a Dove or double-headed Eagle, as emblems of the Holy Spirit, or by the Madonna and her Son. An old Abbot of St. Augustine's, Canterbury, bought one for the choir of his church as long ago as 1097 *'in partibus transmarinis,'* which he describes as *'candelabrum magnum in choro aereum quod Jesse vocatur.'*

Such then being the familiarity and prominence of this type of the Incarnation, let us consider how it was recalled in Nature by certain trees and herbs in the daily life of men. Among the flora the name seems usually connected with those whose stems are long and bare until at the end they burst into flower, or with those whose sides are studded with blossoms, but in art it is usually either a Vine or a Rose that springs from the loins of the sleeping patriarch Jacob, giving forth as it rises upwards to the various chief persons in the royal line that lead to Jesse and his son David. At the summit in the chalice of a flower repose either the emblems of the Holy Spirit—the double-headed Eagle or the Dove, or else there stands the Mother with her Divine Son.

We find the name of *Vara di Jesé* or Rod of Jesse given in Spain to the Tuberose (*Polianthes tuberosa*) whose long bare rod rises several feet from the ground and at its summit is thickly studded with the flowers of this deliciously scented dweller; and the same land carried the name to the Philippine Islands and gave it to the *Dracaena terminalis* of a similar kind of growth, a plant which has always been a graceful addition to international conservatories and winter gardens. The Spaniard has also called the Holyhock (*Alcaea rosea*) *Varitas de David,* its flowering stem suggesting the stages of a soaring genealogical tree, and the French name for the same, of *Baton de Jacob* and probably our own Holly or Holyhocke may have originated in a similar connection. Those plants which now simply bear the name of Rod or Staff of Jacob had possibly the same reference as the Jesse-tree, for the patriarch's homage to the top of his staff was an act of faith in the coming Messias, the staff being the patriarchal sceptre whose flower was Christ, the end and completion of the house of Jacob. It is likely that it is this that led men to name the climbing flower-stalk of Yellow Asphodel Jacob's Rod or Staff, just as in France it remains *Le Baton* or *La Verge de Jacob*. Many a *Campanula* is not only Jacob's Rod but also Mary's Bell, and the species known as *Persicifolia* is the *Baton de Jacob* in France and the *Rosa Mystica* of Verona and Northern Italy. The small *Erigeron Alpinus* in Iceland called *Jakobsfiffil* is a similar example, while in Cumberland the Great Mullein or *Verbascum* is as well-known as Jacob's Staff as elsewhere it is Mary's Taper.

But we believe that it is in the Mistletoe (*Viscum album*) that this type of the *'Virga de radice Jesse'* was illustrated by our Christian forefathers in northern lands, and that it is to this that we may attribute the prominence amid the Yule-tyde greenery. It has been the custom of late years to exclude the Mistletoe from church decorations probably for reasons of propriety, and to retain it in the homes of the people, but it certainly was not the habit of mediæval days to have in the one what was discountenanced in the other; the home was but the reflex of the church; the habit of life, the customs and domestic rites of the one were the expression of the dogmas and ritual of the other, and you could not be pagan in one and Christian in the other with any sincerity to the time. The old Druid reverence for the Mistletoe would strengthen, not lessen the interest with which Christians regarded it when once they perceived in the weird parasite an emblem of one of their own dogmas, for they would feel that other forms of faith had also recognized something uncommon and remarkable in it, and they would find in that very fact a foreshadowing of the strivings of their pagan ancestors through natural religion to attain to truths which to them were assured by revelation; moreover, as far as our imperfect knowledge will allow us to judge, this Druid reverence for the Mistletoe bough was prompted by the same mystery which led to its Christian interpretation and may have even suggested its application. If investigation were made it would probably be found that the exclusion of the Mistletoe from the church has no authority in ancient practice. A writer in the *Folklore Journal* (for December 1896) remarks that in Staffordshire, and 'in the Black Country it was formerly used to decorate churches.' 'Mr. Lawley [also] quotes entries of payments for Mistletoe for this purpose from Churchwardens' Accounts at Bilston in 1672 and Darlaston in 1801.' We might also add that Gay in his *Trivia* bids us

> Now with bright Holly all the temples strow,
> With Laurel green and sacred Mistletoe,

thus testifying that in his day its banishment was not needful.

The Mistletoe furnished a singularly striking and arrestive emblem of the doctrine of the Incarnation. The Saturday office of the Blessed Virgin throughout the year, as well as the teaching of the Nativity itself, vividly impressed upon the minds of the faithful the mystery of God springing from a human source, perfect God and perfect man. In the Mistletoe which Nature gave them to become most verdant in winter they beheld a rod springing from Jesse's stem, an ordinary tree having upon it an offshoot different and unlike any other it produced; a golden bough distinct and peculiar to everything the old stock had ever seen or known before; an innovation, it seemed, of natural law, for though taking fibre and substance from the womb of the parent tree, it possessed a nature and essence quite different, and an origin apart from the wood upon which it grew. No one wandering through the woods in winter when all the trees were leafless, and seeing a branch of fresh Mistletoe shooting forth from some lichen-covered trunk, could fail to recognize the beautiful emblem it was of the Rod of Jesse arising in vigour amid a world of death from a source which looked like unto its fellows. . . .

The words of a hymn attributed to St. Ambrose and used in the ancient Cistercian Breviary seem almost written within sight of the Mistletoe bough, for it is only recently that the mystery of how the shrub is propagated has been discovered.

> *Non ex virili semine*
> *Sed mystico spiramine*
> *Verbum Dei factum est Caro*
> *Fructus quae ventris floruit.*

Just as the Incarnation was the greatest gift of God to man's spiritual needs, so was this emblem of it in Nature potent in his bodily ones. Not only was it deemed protective by its presence against all lightning, witchcraft, phantoms, and evil spirits, but it occupied a very real place in the pharmacy of early days as sovran in epilepsy, and it does so still. In Wales they still call epilepsy 'The rod of Christ,' from the use of Mistletoe in its cure, a name for it found also in other parts of Europe, but it was more popularly known as St. Valentine's sickness, and that saint's memory seems inextricably interwoven in thought with lovers and their pastimes. But the connection between epilepsy and St. Valentine arose in days when faith was strong and medical science weak, when it was the habit to have some saint allied to each complaint to whom the poor sufferers might go as their daysman with the Great Physician, and hence this disease became known as the *Mal di S. Valentine, Veltenstanz* or *Danse de St. Gui.* This use of the shrub in St. Valentine's sickness will explain how that saint in France is often spoken of as St. Gui or St. Mistletoe; but it is not from this connection that it has obtained the association most popularly now united to its presence. It is exceedingly probable that the custom of saluting beneath the Mistletoe had its origin in the practice of giving the Pax universally at this the great feast of Reconciliation of God to man. This salutation has now for many centuries been restricted in the West to the clergy or ecclesiastical bodies, but formerly, as in Russia once, it was the habit at the Christmas Mass for the congregation to salute each other with such words as 'Christ is born to-day,' and after bowing to kiss each other on the cheek or place their lips on the little metal tablet known as a Pax which was passed from one to another. In many old pictures, such as that of the Nativity by Botticelli, the angels with olive boughs are represented as saluting the shepherds as typical of the peace sent from Heaven to men of goodwill, and it is not at all improbable that in former times the interchange of a salute and taking a berry from the Mistletoe-type of the Incarnate Prince of Peace was a token of good-feeling at this season. Stukeley, in his *Medallic History of Carausius,* speaks of a custom that existed 'lately at York' and 'still preserved in the North,' of carrying a bough of 'Mistletoe to the high altar of the cathedral,' and proclaiming towards the four quarters of the earth a general freedom and liberty. We cannot learn anything further than this concerning the custom now apparently forgotten, but it reads very like what may be seen upon New Year's Eve at Notre Dame in Paris, when the archbishop, on behalf of himself and the clergy of his diocese, pronounces solemnly from the high altar the *'Amende honorable,'* in fulfilment of the angelic salutation, *'In terra pax hominibus bonae voluntatis.'*

. . .

The Incarnation being the union of Heaven to earth, of God to man, it was symbolised by the Ladder of the patriarch Jacob's vision, and since Mary was the means by which this union took place, this type of the *Scala Coeli* became one of her titles. In many parts of Europe it was a tradition that at the moment that marks the Saviour's birth, the high heavens open, and the scene of Jacob's vision is once again repeated of angels descending to earth. Many a folklore tale exists of heavenly visitants coming to man under the guise of the wayfarer at the Christmas season, and no petitioner was ever turned away from the door unrelieved by an alms, lest it might perchance be some divine person in reality.

Although there is no flower employed at Christmas which bears the name of this type of the Incarnation, still there are two or three that come later in the year by which they recalled this title. That most generally known in northern Europe is the useful common border-plant called Greek Valerian (*Polemonium coeruleum*), the *Himmels-* or *Jakobs-leiter* of Germany; the *Echelle de Jacob* of France; *Jakobssteige* or *-stige* of Sweden and Denmark. It has the same names with us and also that of Herb Charity, the first of the virtues mentioned by St. Paul in his Ladder of human Perfection which was often frescoed upon church walls. The *Polemonium* has a stem that rises eighteen or twenty inches high with foliage branching from either side of it in regularly successive stages, and mounting upwards to a spike of purplish-blue or white flowers; and although it seems to be better known as Greek Valerian, it has no kind of affinity with that family of herbs.

The old botanical title of *Scala Coeli* is also borne by the Solomon's Seal (*Polygonatum multiflorum*), which is still spoken of as Jacob's Ladder, and since each pair of leaflets is accompanied by the interesting flower of this beautiful herb, it made a very pretty parable of the progressive stages in the life of virtue. In France the *Persicaria* (*Polygonum orientale*) has the name of *La Montée au Ciel,* and in Shropshire the Jacob's Ladder is the Greater Celandine (*Chelidonium majus*), while in Devonshire the spire of the Larkspur is so known (*Delphinium*), but perhaps their enumeration is sufficient to show at least that the title was once a familiar one.

.   .   .

It was a favourite practice of the graphic artists of mediæval times to oppose type and antitype for the consideration of the faithful. In such works as the *Biblia Pauperum* we see the Old Testament type of Moses before the fiery thorn on Sinai corresponding to the New Testament antitype of the Holy Babe in the cradle at Bethlehem, or in the ancient glass left in Canterbury's Cathedral Church *'Moses cum Rubo'* has its complement in *'Angelus cum Maria,'* while beneath is the ejaculation *'Rubus non consumitur, tua nec comburitur in carne virginitas.'*

This was one of the most prominent types of the immaculate purity of the Virgin Mother at the Incarnation and Birth of her Lord and Son, and would belong more strictly perchance to her flora if it were not so inseparably connected with the offices and the greenery employed at the Feast of the Nativity. In the former we have one of the 'great O Antiphons' in the novena, beginning *'O Adonai, et Dux domus Israel, Qui Moysi in igne flammae Rubi apparuisti,'* etc., to which at the octave the fulfilment is given, *Rubum quem viderat Moyses incombustum conservatam agnovimus tuam laudibilem virginitatem sancta Dei genitrix.'* For Mary was the Bush on fire with the Holy Spirit, that concealed the Deity and gave Him human shape and substance and yet remained a Virgin. One of Chaucer's addresses to her is that invocation in the *Prioress's Tale,* beginning—

O Mother Maid! O Maid and Mother free!
O Bush unburnt burning in Moses' sight!

or as he says in the 'A.B.C.'—

Moises, that saugh the Bush with flaumes rede
Brenninge, of which ther never a stikke brende,
Was singe of thyn unwemmed maidenhede.
Thou art the bush on which ther gan descende
The Holy Gost, the which that Moises wende
Had ben a-fyr; and this was in a figure.
Now Lady, from the fyr thou us defende
Which that in helle eternally shal dure.

It was once a favourite device for ecclesiastical artists, both in the East and West, to depict or carve the Mother and Son enthroned in a tree of flame, and few motives could be so full of inspiration for both the designer and beholder, yet, like the rich tracery of the Jesse-tree, we seldom or never see it employed in modern work; both contain quite unlimited scope for decorative purposes, whether in stone, glass, or embroidery, and seem complements of each other in their dogmatic teaching; while the trees and herbs that have been associated with them in Nature are also highly capable of artistic treatment.

The especial tree which we, in northern latitudes, have chosen as our type of the Burning Bush is the Holly or Holy Tree (*Ilex aquifolium*), one which we have pre-eminently called the 'Christmas' bush, and which seems peculiarly suitable to the people of England and America. . . . It is certainly the most pictorially effective ornament that winter spares to us, delighting the eye as it gracefully rises from the virgin snow with its white stem, deep green leaves and scarlet fruit. In the silent woods when the snow lies on the ground like Nature's pall spread over her vast sleeping place, when all the trees are bare save for the oak's sered and fluttering leaves, then we may see in the Holly a picture of joyous hope. Its glossy foliage bent into varying planes produces a play of light and shade that gives a singular life to the tree's appearance, while its blaze of fiery berries set in thick clusters against the deep green background, made men see in it a beautiful illustration of one of their favourite types. In old Cornwall it was once known as 'Aunt' Mary's Tree, the title of Modryb Marya being given to it, according to the late Mr. Hawker of Moorwinstow, in tender respect for the Mother of God. He explains that the household names uncle and aunt were uttered and used in the west country in the same manner as they are in many countries in the East to this day, not as phrases of kindred, but as words of kindly greeting and regard, and that it was this that suggested the name of Modryb Marya for Mary on the Tamar side. In his *Cornish Ballads,* Hawker has written a very charming carol to the Holly, 'the tree with the bleeding breast' as he calls it, and there are many old ones to be found in praise of this favourite; its symbolism, and its affording food and shelter for the birds in winter, apart from its beauty, made it to be loved by the poets, and affection for it found vent in such old proverbial sayings as—

> Whosoever agaynst Holly do crye
> In a lepe shall he hang full hye.
> Whosoever agaynst Holly do sing
> He may wepe and his hands wring.

In France it is known as *Epine de Christ;* in Germany as *Christdorn,* and in Norway, Sweden and Denmark as the same; but there are some other names which exist for it in France that need explanation. It is very widely known as *Le grand Pardon,* and in Provence as *Garrus de la Santo Baumo* : the latter title refers to its growing at the famous convent of the Holy Cave of St. Mary Magdalene between Toulon and Marseilles, but whether the former be connected with this place of pilgrimage or the Christmas festival we cannot be sure. If the Holly-tree emblem of the Burning Bush recalled to men's minds the Maiden Mother, the sharp crisping of its leaves also told them of the spiny crown that awaited that Mother's Son.

The Wild Myrtle, Box Holly, or Butcher's Broom, as the *Ruscus aculeatus* is variously styled, is as popular in use at the Nativity in southern Europe as the *Ilex aquifolium* is elsewhere. It is one of the shrubs always to be seen employed in Spain and Italy, and to be found near the Christmas cribs or pietas of every household. It grows abundantly in our copses and hedge-rows, and, together with other varieties, such as the *Ruscus racemosus* or Alexandrian Laurel, should be more cultivated in our gardens to furnish us with winter greenery of a beautiful as well as of an interesting character. Its bright scarlet berries make it attractive; but it also possesses the singular property of giving off an inflammable gas which is said to be ignitable under certain conditions of the atmosphere, and this made it a very remarkable representative of the Burning Bush. In Provençal France it is essentially known as *Calendau* or 'Christmas,' just in the same way as our Holly is in England, while in the Balearic Isles its fruit is spoken of as *Ciceretas del Bon Pastor,* which may have some reference to our Lord's title or to the Bethlehem shepherds. These trees are often to be found in Lancashire cottage gardens, where they are called 'Jerusalem Thorns,' and have usually connected with them there the story of the Glastonbury Thorn, being said to flower upon the night of the Saviour's birth.

A favourite old plant, once to be found in most old garden plots where soil was light and dry, was the Wild Dittany or *Fraxinella* (*Dictamnus*), which is still known to our peasantry as the Burning Bush. It is a native of the Taurus and Caucasus, but seems to have been introduced into England for a considerable length of time, and is certainly deserving of a place in every flower enclosure. Its erect stems form pleasant masses of foliage, rising about two feet, and its racemes of purplish or white flowers appear about midsummer. When these dense tufts of blossom have faded, the seed-vessels are found to be eminently

44

aromatic and resinous, and the whole plant exhales an ætheric vapour, so powerful that if a candle be brought near to it the air around will burst into flame of greater or less intensity, and thus afford a remarkable illustration of its name.

At the convent upon Mount Sinai and in the East generally, the species of Acacia known as the *Acacia seneh* is identified with the real Bush of Fire, and it is curious to mark how the traditions of the East connected with the Acacias have in the West become allied to the Hawthorns. In this instance we find in France that the Pink Hawthorn (*Crataegus pyracantha*) is known as *L'Arbre de Moise* or *Buisson ardent,* and in Cheshire as the Egyptian Thorn; and its thickly powdered head of the exquisite pink blossom renders the name singularly appropriate. For the same reason we find the title of *Buisson ardent* conveyed to the Mauritius where the rosy-flowered *Ixora* is so known, and probably many other modern examples might be found.

Mateo de Cerezo painted a picture for the Franciscan Friars of Valladolid, in which he placed the Blessed Virgin seated in a cherry-tree : it may have been as a play upon his own name, and to indicate the place he desired his patroness to occupy in his heart, but there is a species of Cherry (*Cerasus pyracantha*) known as the Burning Bush, and perhaps the artist united both meanings in one. . . .

ALFRED E. P. RAYMUND DOWLING

i

Sir,—

I am a young Woman, and have my Fortune to make, for which Reason I come constantly to Church to hear divine Service, and make Conquests; but one great Hindrance in this my Design is, that our Clerk, who was once a Gardener, has this Christmas so over-decked the Church with Greens, that he has quite spoil'd my Prospect, insomuch that I have scarce seen the young Baronet I dress at these three Weeks, though we have both been very Constant at our Devotions, and do not sit above three Pews off. The Church, as it is now equipped, looks more like a Green-house than a Place of Worship; the middle Isle is a very pretty Shady Walk, and the Pews look like so many Arbours on each Side of it. The Pulpit itself has such Clusters of Ivy, Holly, and Rosemary about it, that a light Fellow in our Pew took Occasion to say, that the Congregation heard the Word out of a Bush, like *Moses.* Sir *Anthony Love's* Pew in particular is so well hedg'd, that all my Batteries have no Effect. I am obliged to shoot at Random among the Boughs, without taking any Manner of Aim. Mr. *Spectator,* unless you will give Orders for removing these Greens, I shall grow a very aukward Creature at Church, and soon have little Else to do there but say my Prayers. I am in Haste,

Dear Sir,

Your most obedient Servant,

Jenny Simper

ii

Sir,—

I am Clerk of the Parish from whence Mrs. *Simper* sends her Complaint, in your yesterday's *Spectator.* I must beg of you to publish this as a publick Admonition to the aforesaid Mrs. *Simper,* otherwise all my honest Care in the Disposition of the Greens in the Church will have no Effect: I shall therefore with your Leave lay before you the whole Matter. I was formerly, as she charges me, for several Years a Gardener in the County of *Kent;* but I must absolutely deny, that it is out of any Affection I retain for my old Employment that I have placed my Greens so liberally about the Church, but out of a Particular

Spleen I conceived against Mrs. *Simper,* and others of the same Sisterhood, some Time ago. As to herself, I had one Day set the hundredth Psalm, and was singing the first Line in order to put the Congregation into the Tune, she was all the While curtsying to Sir *Anthony,* in so affected and indecent a Manner, that the Indignation I conceiv'd made me forget myself so far, as from the Tune of that Psalm to wander into *Southwell*-tune, and from thence into *Windsor*-tune, still unable to recover myself, until I had with the utmost Confusion set a new one. Nay, I have often seen her rise up and smile, and curtsy to one at the Lower End of the Church, in the midst of a *Gloria-Patri;* and when I have spoke the Assent to a Prayer with a long *Amen,* uttered with a Decent Gravity, she has been rolling her Eyes about in such a Manner, as plainly shew'd, however she was moved, it was not towards an Heavenly Object. In fine, she extended her Conquests so far over the Males, and rais'd such Envy in the Females, that what between Love of those, and the Jealousy of these, I was almost the only Person that looked in a Prayer-book all Church-time. I had several Projects in my Head to put a Stop to this Growing Mischief; but as I have long lived in *Kent,* and there often heard how the *Kentish* men evaded the Conquerour, by carrying green Boughs over their Heads, it put me in Mind of practising this Device against Mrs. *Simper.* I find I have preserv'd many a Young Man from her Eye-shot by this Means; therefore humbly pray the Boughs may be fix'd, until she shall give Security for her Peaceable Intentions.

Your humble Servant,
Francis Sternhold

RICHARD STEELE, 1671–1729

THE REVEREND DOCTOR OPIMIAM SPEAKS ...

I LIKE the idea of the Yule log, the enormous block of wood, carefully selected long before, and preserved where it would be thoroughly dry, which burned on the old-fashioned hearth. It would not suit the stoves of our modern saloons. We could not burn it in our kitchens, where a small fire in the midst of a mass of black iron, roasts, and bakes, and boils, and steams, and broils, and fries, by a complicated apparatus, which, whatever may be

its other virtues, leaves no space for a Christmas fire. I like the
festoons of holly on the walls and windows; the dance under the
mistletoe; the gigantic sausage; the baron of beef; the vast
globe of plum-pudding, the true image of the earth, flattened at
the poles; the tapping of the old hall, when the squire and his
household and his neighbourhood were as one. I like the idea
of what has gone, and I can still enjoy the reality of what
remains.

THOMAS LOVE PEACOCK, 1785–1866

HARD FROST

Frost called to water 'Halt!'
And crusted the moist snow with sparkling salt;
Brooks, their own bridges, stop,
And icicles in long stalactites drop,
And tench in water-holes
Lurk under gluey glass like fish in bowls.

In the hard-rutted lane
At every footstep breaks a brittle pane,
And tinkling trees ice-bound,
Changed into weeping willows, sweep the ground;
Dead boughs take root in ponds
And ferns on windows shoot their ghostly fronds.

But vainly the fierce frost
Interns poor fish, ranks trees in an armed host,
Hangs daggers from house-eaves
And on the windows ferny ambush weaves;
In the long war grown warmer
The sun will strike him dead and strip his armour.

ANDREW YOUNG, 1885–

SUDDEN THAWS

THAWS are sometimes surprisingly quick, considering the small quantity of rain. Does not the warmth at such times come from below? The cold in still, severe seasons seems to come down from above, for the coming over of a cloud in severe nights raises the thermometer abroad at once full ten degrees. The first notices of thaws often seem to appear in vaults, cellars, etc.

If a frost happens, even when the ground is considerably dry, as soon as a thaw takes place, the paths and fields are all in a batter. Country people say that the frost draws moisture. But the true philosophy is, that the steam and vapours continually ascending from the earth, are bound in by the frost, and not suffered to escape till released by the thaw. No wonder then that the surface is all in a float; since the quantity of moisture by evaporation that arises daily from every acre of ground is astonishing.

GILBERT WHITE, 1720–93

DUCKS AND GEESE

Among the tawny tasselled reed
The ducks and ducklings float and feed.
With head oft dabbling in the flood
They fish all day the weedy mud,
And tumbler-like are bobbing there,
Heels topsy turvy in the air.
The geese in troops come droving up,
Nibble the weeds, and take a sup;
And, closely puzzled to agree,
Chatter like gossips over tea.
The gander with his scarlet nose
When strife's at height will interpose;
And, stretching neck to that and this,
With now a mutter, now a hiss,
A nibble at the feathers too,
A sort of 'pray be quiet do,'
And turning as the matter mends
He stills them into mutual friends;

49

Then in a sort of triumph sings
And throws the water o'er his wings.

JOHN CLARE, 1793-1864

THE TURKEY

He moves about as ship prepared to sail,
He hoists his proud rotundity of tail,
The half-seal'd eyes and changeful neck he shows,
Where, in its quick'ning colours, vengeance glows;
From red to blue the pendent wattles turn,
Blue mix'd with red, as matches when they burn;
And thus th' intruding snarler to oppose,
Urged by enkindling wrath, he gobbling goes.

GEORGE CRABBE, 1754-1832

PROVISIONS

Winter draws out what summer laid in.

SIR THOMAS FULLER, 1608-61

GOOD FARE

N O W Capons and Hennes, besides Turkies, Geese and Duckes, besides Beefe and Mutton, must all die for the great feast, for in twelve days a multitude of people will not bee fed with a little : now plummes and spice, Sugar and Honey, square it among pies and broth, and Gossip I drinke to you, and you are welcome, and I thanke you, and how doe you, and I pray you bee merrie : nowe are the Taylors and the Tiremakers full of worke against the Holidayes, and Musicke must bee in tune, or else never : the youth must dance and sing, and the aged sit by the fire.

NICHOLAS BRETON, 1545–1626

WASSAYLE

Wassayle, wassayle, out of the mylke pale,
Wassayle, wassayle, as white as my nayle,
Wassayle, wassayle, in snow, froste and hayle,
Wassayle, wassayle, with partriche and rayle,
Wassayle, wassayle, that much doth avayle,
Wassayle, wassayle, that never will fayle.

JOHN BALE, 1495–1563

RECIPE FOR STEWED TURKEY

P U T in a large stew-kettle half a pound of bacon cut in slices, four ounces of knuckle of veal, three sprigs of parsley, two of thyme, a bay-leaf, six small onions, one carrot cut in four pieces, three cloves, one clove of garlic, salt, pepper, and then the turkey; wet with a pint of white wine, same of broth, cover as near air-tight as you can, place in a moderately-heated oven or on a moderate fire, let simmer (not boil) about two hours and a half, then turn it over, put back on the fire or in the oven for another two hours and a half, after which dish the turkey; strain the sauce and put it back on the fire to reduce it to a jelly, which you spread on it, and serve.

NORMAN DOUGLAS, 1868–1952

HOW TO SERVE UP BOAR'S HEAD

At Christmas time be careful of your Fame,
See the old Tenant's Table be the same;
Then if you wou'd send up the Brawner's Head,
Sweet Rosemary and Bays around it spread:
His foaming tusks let some large Pippin grace,
Or 'midst these thund'ring Spears an Orange place,
Sauce like himself, offensive to its Foes,
The Roguish Mustard, dang'rous to the Nose.
Sack and well-spic'd *Hippocras* the Wine,
Wassail the Bowl with antient Ribbands fine,
Porridge with Plumbs, and Turkeys with the Chine. . . .

WILLIAM KING, 1663–1712

A DISH FOR A POET

TAKE a large olive, stone it and then stuff it with a paste made of anchovy, capers, and oil.

Put the olive inside a trussed and boned bec-figue (garden warbler).

Put the bec-figue inside a fat ortolan.

Put the ortolan inside a boned lark.

Put the stuffed lark inside a boned thrush.

Put the thrush inside a fat quail.

Put the quail, wrapped in vine-leaves, inside a boned lapwing.

Put the lapwing inside a boned golden plover.

Put the plover inside a fat, boned, red-legged partridge.

Put the partridge inside a young, boned, and well-hung wood-cock.

Put the woodcock, rolled in bread-crumbs, inside a boned teal.

Put the teal inside a boned guinea-fowl.

Put the guinea-fowl, well larded, inside a young and boned tame duck.

Put the duck inside a boned and fat fowl.

Put the fowl inside a well-hung pheasant.

Put the pheasant inside a boned and fat wild goose.

Put the goose inside a fine turkey.

Put the turkey inside a boned bustard.

Having arranged your roast after this fashion, place it in a large saucepan with onions stuffed with cloves, carrots, small squares of ham, celery, mignonette, several strips of bacon well-seasoned, pepper, salt, spice, coriander seeds, and two cloves of garlic.

Seal the saucepan hermetically by closing it with pastry. Then put it for ten hours over a gentle fire, and arrange it so that the heat can penetrate evenly. An oven moderately heated will suit better than the hearth.

Before serving, remove the pastry, put the roast on a hot dish after having removed the grease—if there is any—, and serve.

TRADITIONAL, c. 1814

CARVING

HAVE you learned to carve? for it is ridiculous not to carve well. A man who tells you gravely that he cannot carve, may as well tell you that he cannot blow his nose; it is both as necessary and as easy.

PHILIP DORMER STANHOPE, 1694–1773

SENATORIAL PORT

SENATORIAL Port! we say. We cannot say that of any other wine. Port is deep-sea deep. It is in its flavour deep; mark the difference. It is like a classic tragedy, organic in conception. An ancient Hermitage has the light of the antique; the merit that it can grow to an extreme old age; a merit. Neither of Hermitage nor of Hock can you say that it is the blood of those long years, retaining the strength of youth with the wisdom of age. To Port for that! Port is our noblest legacy! Observe I do not compare the wines; I distinguish the qualities. Let them live together for our enrichment; they are not rivals like the Idæan Three.

GEORGE MEREDITH, 1828–1909

THE BANKER'S SECRET

Can name his claret—if he sees the cork.

OLIVER WENDELL HOLMES, 1809–94

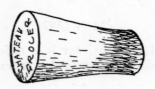

SEVENTEENTH CENTURY CHARMES
i. For Stenching Blood

Jesus, that was of a Virgin born,
Was pricked both with nail and thorn;
It neither wealed, nor belled, rankled nor boned;
In the name of Jesus no more shall this.

ii. For Killing Cramp

Cramp be thou faintless
As our Lady was sinless,
When she bare Jesus.   TRADITIONAL

A WINTER RAINBOW

Dec. 15, 1804. Saw the limb of a rainbow footing itself on the
sea at a small apparent distance from the shore, a thing of itself
—no substrate cloud or even mist visible—but the distance
glimmered through it as through a thin semi-transparent hoop.

S. T. COLERIDGE, 1772–1834

A RAINBOW CUTTLEFISH

I FOUND a strange fish on the shore with rainbows about
its wild staring eyes, enclosed in a sort of sack with long
tentacula beautifully coloured, quite dead, but when I took it
up by the tail it spotted all the sand underneath with great drops
of ink, so I suppose it was a kind of cuttlefish. I found too a pale
pink orchis on the sea bank and a pink vetch, a low sort of shrub
with here and there a thorn.

ALFRED LORD TENNYSON, 1809–92

A FESTIVE SOLITUDE

WHEN I was scarce old enough to understand, I heard read by the fireside some Tennyson. Tonight I have taken down the volume, and the voice of so long ago has read to me once again—read as no other ever did, that voice which taught me to know poetry, the voice which never spoke to me but of good and noble things. Would I have those accents overborne by a living tongue, however welcome its sound at another time? Jealously I guard my Christmas solitude.

GEORGE GISSING, 1857–1903

NO SOLSTICE

I HATE and loathe winter and everything about it—its beef, its balls, its parties, its mincepies, its puddings, its sweetmeats, its exhibitions, its Bank holidays, its home holidays, its rain, wind, cold, sleet, frost, fog, iced baths, snow, slush, mud, charities, clerical opportunities, newspaper retrospects, bon-bons, crackers—all, each, I do so hate, and at any cost wish myself out of, that I have really not been decent or presentable, and have sulked and kept indoors these many days.

EDWARD BURNE-JONES, 1833–98

POLITE CONVERSATION

Coming! ay, so is Christmas.

JONATHAN SWIFT, 1667–1745

TALKING MAKES IT SO

They talk of Christmas so long that it comes.

GEORGE HERBERT, 1593–1633

A WEATHER PESSEMIST

22nd Dec., 1836: The weather is beautiful; but as Noodle says (with his eyes beaming with delight), 'We shall suffer for this, sir, by-and-by.'

SYDNEY SMITH, 1771–1845

SIR ROGER'S OPEN HOUSE

HE afterwards fell into an Account of the Diversions which had passed in his House during the Holidays; for Sir *Roger,* after the laudable Custom of his Ancestors, always keeps open House at Christmas. I learned from him that he had killed eight Fat Hogs for this Season, that he had dealt about his Chines very liberally amongst his Neighbours, and that in particular he had sent a string of Hogs' puddings with a Pack of Cards to every poor Family in the Parish. I have often thought, says Sir *Roger,* it happens very well that Christmas should fall out in the Middle of Winter. It is the most dead uncomfortable Time of the Year, when the poor People would suffer very much from their Poverty and Cold, if they had not good Cheer, warm Fires, and Christmas Gambols to support them. I love to rejoice their poor Hearts at this Season, and to see the whole village merry in my great Hall. I allow a double Quantity of Malt to my Small Beer, and

57

set it a-running for twelve Days to every one that calls for it. I have always a Piece of Cold Beef and Mince-pye upon the Table, and am wonderfully pleased to see my Tenants pass away a whole Evening in playing their innocent Tricks, and smutting one another. Our Friend Will *Wimble* is as merry as any of them, and shews a thousand Roguish Tricks upon these Occasions. . . .

JOSEPH ADDISON, 1672–1719

IS THERE A SANTA CLAUS?

N O T believe in Santa Claus! You might as well not believe in fairies. . . . Nobody sees Santa Claus, but that is no sign there is no Santa Claus. The most real things in the world are those which neither children nor men can see. No Santa Claus! Thank God! he lives and he lives forever.

New York Sun, 1897

CHANUKAH—OR THE FEAST OF LIGHTS

I T was dark by four in midwinter, and coming home from school in the December dusk to tea in the dining-room with the fire blazing and the red silk shade of the low-hanging chandelier lit up by the bulbs inside, one was conscious of a theatrical shift in scene, as of a curtain lifted. And in the streets outside, the little fruitshops and fancy goods stores and grocers, decorated for the Christmas season, with mounds of tangerines set in half-globes of silver paper, with net stockings filled with cheap toys and bells of coloured paper hanging in the window, would repeat the theme in a different key: festive windows lit in the darkness to challenge the December murk. On a clear day the dusk would turn true violet in colour, and the dark outline of the Castle would stand out on the horizon in romantic gloom. (Many years later they took to floodlighting it, which was picturesque but not the same thing: the gas light in the windows of the little shops in the back streets, with their tinsel decorations and cheap Christmas goods, was the most moving illumination I ever saw in Edinburgh.) We did not observe Christmas, of course; we kept instead the more or less contemporary Jewish festival of *Chanukah*; but the Christmas atmosphere always seemed proper and acceptable, and it never seemed to me that I was in any way cut off from it in virtue of our not keeping the actual day. And the coloured *Chanukah* candles, and my father's tenor voice leading us in the old hymn of *maoz tsur,* 'Rock of Ages,' mingled in my mind with the illuminated windows, with the silver tangerines and the boxes of crackers and the loops of tinsel, with the old Castle looming black in the purple evening and the sense of the darkening city beyond falling away to the Firth of Forth. *Chanukah* was Edinburgh in December.

It was strange, I suppose—though it did not seem strange to me then—this easy blending of Christmas and *Chanukah,* of Jewish history and Edinburgh atmosphere. *Chanukah,* the Feast of Lights, commemorates a miracle in the Temple after the successful revolt by Judas Maccabeus and his heroic companions against the paganising forces of Antiochus Epiphanes : when I was fifteen I wrote an 'epic poem' on the subject, modelled, in style and verse form, on Scott's *Marmion.* Yet *Chanukah* to us was also the distribution of 'pokes' of sweets to Jewish children after the special service in the Graham Street synagogue, and walking home afterwards in the dark December evening, savouring the atmosphere of Edinburgh at night during the Christmas season. There was, of course, much less commercial ballyhoo about Christmas then than there is now, and besides, Scotland, whose established Presbyterian Church had long minimised celebration of Christmas Day as 'Popish,' celebrated the season rather than the day. The real Scottish festival was Hogmanay, New Year's Eve, in which we could participate as a purely secular feast. Jewish New Year was a solemn occasion, the ushering in of the period of penitence which culminated in the Day of Atonement ten days later; the Scottish New Year was an utterly different sort of affair, and though we never celebrated it as a family, we were at liberty to identify ourselves with its celebration by others. I am not sure that I have set out all the factors in their proper logical emphasis. Perhaps there were other reasons for what, in retrospect, I can see as the effortless reconciliation of a very Jewish *Chanukah* feeling with a very Edinburgh feeling of celebration. I doubt if I would even have considered this worth commenting on if I had not been struck with the way in which Jewish parents get fussed about the

59

Christmas problem today. It is a problem that I never remember once being bothered about in my childhood. (But no sooner have I written this than I ask myself whether it is wholly and absolutely true. I seem to remember a faint twinge—of regret? of simple envy?—when the red mail vans came up our street, delivering Christmas presents, and I knew they would not stop at our door.)

DAVID DAICHES, 1912–

A CANDLE FOR LUCIA

W H E N it seemed that they must leave on December 13th, James Joyce, in whom an irrational sense of dread was deeply set, tried to change the date, but nothing could be done about it. Giorgio described how with trepidation he went into Vichy to have their passports stamped by the German authorities, for he himself had had no visa. 'Put yours on top,' advised the Frenchman in the waiting-room. 'You might get away with it.' Fortunately there was no investigation but there was still the chance of inspection to be faced on that long, war-dark journey across France.

Thus, on December 13th—the feast of Saint Lucia—exactly a month from the date on which he was to die—Joyce lit a candle for his daughter in the *salle à manger*. 'And the darned thing was burning away all day,' said Giorgio ruefully. 'Then late in the evening we packed ourselves and what was left of our belongings into the only available taxi and drove to take the train at St. Germain-des-Fosses some kilometres away.'

In the little room of the Hotel du Commerce, where so much talk of departure had been heard, the mirror over the chimney-piece continued to reflect for another hour or two the flame of Joyce's offering there.

PATRICIA HUTCHINS, 1911–

SEVENTEENTH CENTURY SAYING

A candle lights others and consumes itself.

TRADITIONAL

HALF AWAKE

There is a bird, they say,
That only sings
When snow is on the way,
And the moon ice-cold.
His name is so old
That now his name is lost
But I have heard
His nest is made of frost.
His singing seems
For any human ear
Almost too cold to hear
Yet I was told
With other far-off things
In dreams
About this bird.

FRANCES CORNFORD, 1886–

BIRD OF DAWNING

Some say that ever 'gainst that season comes
Wherein our Saviour's birth is celebrated,
The bird of dawning singeth all night long:
And then, they say, no spirit dare stir abroad,
The nights are wholesome, then no planets strike,
No fairy takes nor witch hath power to charm,
So hallow'd and so gracious is the time.

WILLIAM SHAKESPEARE, 1564–1616

SHAKESPEARE AND CHRISTMAS:
BY FR–NK H–RR–S

[THE passage by Marcellus on the Elsinore ramparts about the 'bird of dawning' is] the best that Shakespeare can vamp up for the birthday of the Man with whom he of all men had the most in common. And Dryasdust, eternally unable to distinguish chalk from cheese, throws up his hands in admiration of the marvellous poetry. If Dryasdust had written it, it would more than pass muster. But as coming from Shakespeare, how feeble-cold—aye, and sulky-sinister! The greatest praiser the world will ever know! —and all he can find in his heart to sing of Christmas is a stringing-together of old women's superstitions! Again and again he has painted Winter for us as it never has been painted since—never by Goethe even, though Goethe in more than one of the *Winter-Lieder* touched the hem of his garment. There was every external reason why he should sing, as only he could have sung, of Christmas. The Queen set great store by it. She and her courtiers celebrated it year by year with lusty-pious unction. And thus the ineradicable snob in Shakespeare had the most potent of all inducements to honour the feast with the full power that was in him. But he did not, because he would not. What is the key to the enigma?

For many years I hunted it vainly. The second time that I met Carlyle I tried to enlist his sympathy and aid. He sat pensive for a while and then said that it seemed to him 'a goose-quest.' I replied, 'You have always a phrase for everything, Tom, but always the wrong one.' He covered his face, and presently, peering at me through his gnarled fingers, said 'Mon, ye're recht.' I discussed the problem with Renan, with Emerson, with Disraeli, also with Cetewayo—poor Cetewayo, best and bravest of men, but intellectually a Professor, like the rest of them. It was borne in on me that if I were to win to the heart of the mystery I must win alone.

The solution, when suddenly it dawned on me, was so simple-stark that I was ashamed of the ingenious-clever ways I had been following. (I learned then—and perhaps it is the one lesson worth the learning of any man—that truth may be approached only through the logic of the heart. For the heart is eye and ear, and all excellent understanding abides there.) On Christmas Day, assuredly, Anne Hathaway was born.

In what year she was born I do not know nor care. I take it she was not less than thirty-eight when she married Shakespeare. This, however, is sheer conjecture, and in no way important-apt to our inquiry. It is not the year, but the day of the year, that matters. All we need bear in mind is that on Christmas Day that woman was born into the world.

If there be any doubting Thomas among my readers, let him not be afraid to utter himself. I am (with the possible exception of Shakespeare) the gentlest man that ever breathed, and I do but bid him study the Plays in the light I have given him. The first thing that will strike him is that Shakespeare's thoughts turned constantly to the birthdays of all his Fitton-heroines, as a lover's thoughts always do turn to the moment at which the loved one first saw the light. 'There was a star danced, and under that' was born Beatrice. Juliet was born 'on Lammas Eve.' Marina tells us she derived her name from the chance of her having been 'born at sea.' And so on, throughout the whole gamut of women in whom Mary Fitton was bodied forth to us. But mark how carefully Shakespeare says never a word about the birthdays of the various shrews and sluts in whom, again and again, he gave us his wife. When and where was born Queen Constance, the scold? And Bianca? And Doll Tearsheet, and 'Greasy Jane' in the song, and all the rest of them? It is of the last importance that we should know. Yet never a hint is vouchsafed us in the text. It is clear that Shakespeare cannot bring himself to write about Anne

63

Hathaway's birthday—will not stain his imagination by thinking of it. That is entirely human-natural. But why should he loathe Christmas Day itself with precisely the same loathing? There is but one answer—and that inevitable-final. The two days were one.

Some soul-secrets are so terrible that the most hardened realist of us may well shrink from laying them bare. Such a soul-secret was this of Shakespeare's. Think of it! The gentlest spirit that ever breathed, raging and fuming endlessly in impotent-bitter spleen against the prettiest of festivals! Here is a spectacle so tragic-piteous that, try as we will, we shall not put it from us. And it is well that we should not, for in our plenary compassion we shall but learn to love the man the more.

[Mr. Fr—nk H—rr—s is very much a man of genius, and I should be sorry if this adumbration of his manner made any one suppose that I do not rate his writings about Shakespeare higher than those of all 'the Professors' together.—M.B.]

MAX BEERBOHM, 1872–1956

A CAPITAL DISTRIBUTION

CHRISTMAS EVE had been for all the Marriners, except Mr Marriner, a most exhausting day. The head of the house usually got off lightly at the festive season, lightly that is as far as personal effort went. Financially, no; Mr Marriner knew that financially quite a heavy drain was being made on his resources. And later in the evening when he got out his cheque book to give his customary presents to his family, his relations and the staff, the drain would be heavier. But he could afford it, he could afford it better this Christmas than at any other Christmas in the history of his steadily increasing fortune. And he didn't have to think, he didn't have to choose; he only had to consult a list, and add one or two names, and cross off one or two. There was quite a big item to cross off, quite a big item, though it didn't figure on the list or on the counterfoil of his cheque book. If he saw fit he would add the sum so saved to his children's cheques. Jeremy and Anne would then think him even more generous than he was, and if his wife made any comment, which she wouldn't, being a tactful woman, he would laugh and call it a Capital Distribution —'capital in every sense, my dear!'

But this could wait till after dinner.

So of the quartet who sat down to the meal, he was the only one who hadn't spent a laborious day. His wife and Anne had both worked hard decorating the house and making arrangements for the party on Boxing Day. They hadn't spent the time in getting presents, they hadn't had to. Anne, who was two years older than Jeremy, inherited her mother's gift for present-giving and had made her selections weeks ago; she had a sixth sense for knowing what people wanted. But Jeremy had left it all to the last moment. His method was the reverse of Anne's and much less successful; he thought of the present first and the recipient afterwards. Who would this little box do for? Who would this other little box do for? Who should be the fortunate possessor of this third little box? In present-giving his mind followed a one-way track; and this year it was little boxes. They were expensive and undiscriminating presents and he was secretly ashamed of them. Now it was too late to do anything more : but when he thought of the three or four friends who would remain unboxed his conscience smote him.

Silent and self-reproachful, he was the first to hear the singing outside the window.

'Listen, there's some carol singers !' His voice, which was breaking, plunged and croaked.

The others all stopped talking and smiles broke out on their faces.

'Quite good, aren't they?'

'The first we've had this year,' said Mrs Marriner.

'Well, not the first, my dear; they started coming days ago, but I sent them away and said that waits must wait till Christmas Eve.'

'How many of them are there?'

'Two, I think,' said Jeremy.

'A man and a woman?'

Jeremy got up and drew the curtain. Pierced only by a single distant street-lamp, the darkness in the garden pressed against the window-pane.

'I can't quite see,' he said, coming back. 'But I think it's a man and a boy.'

'A man and a boy?' said Mr Marriner. 'That's rather unusual.'

'Perhaps they're choristers, Daddy. They do sing awfully well.'

At that moment the front door bell rang. To preserve the

65

character of the house, which was an old one, they had retained the original brass bell-pull. When it was pulled the whole house seemed to shudder audibly, with a strangely searching sound, as if its heart-strings had been plucked, while the bell itself gave out a high yell, that split into a paroxysm of jangling. The Marriners were used to this phenomenon, and smiled when it made strangers jump: tonight it made them jump themselves. They listened for the sound of footsteps crossing the stone flags of the hall, but there was none.

'Mrs Parfitt doesn't come till washing-up time,' said Mrs Marriner. 'Who'll go and give them something?'

'I will,' Anne said, jumping up. 'What shall I give them, Daddy?'

'Oh, give them a bob,' said Mr Marriner, producing the coin from his pocket. However complicated the sum required he always had it.

Anne set off with the light step and glowing face of an eager benefactor; she came back after a minute or two at a much slower pace and looking puzzled and rather frightened. She didn't sit down but stood over her place with her hands on the chair-back.

'He said it wasn't enough,' she said.

'Wasn't enough?' her father repeated. 'Did he really say that?' Anne nodded.

'Well, I like his cheek.' Even to his family Mr Marriner's moods were unforeseeable; by some chance the man's impudence had touched a sympathetic chord in him. 'Go back and say that if they sing another carol they shall have another bob.'

But Anne didn't move.

'If you don't mind, Daddy, I'd rather not.'

They all three raised questioning faces to hers.

'You'd rather not? Why?'

'I didn't like his manner.'

'Whose, the man's?'

'Yes. The boy—you were right, Jeremy, it is a boy, quite a small boy—didn't say anything.'

'What was wrong with the man's manner?' Mr Marriner, still genial, asked.

'Oh, I don't know!' Anne began to breathe quickly and her fingers tightened on the chair-back. 'And it wasn't only his manner.'

66

'Henry, I shouldn't—' began Mrs Marriner warningly, when suddenly Jeremy jumped up. He saw the chance to redeem himself in his own eyes from his ineffectiveness over the Christmas shopping—from the general ineffectiveness that he was conscious of whenever he compared himself with Anne.

'Here's the shilling,' Anne said, holding it out. 'He wouldn't take it.'

'This will make it two,' their father said, suiting the action to the word. 'But only if they sing again, mind you.'

While Jeremy was away, they all fell silent, Anne still trying to compose her features, Mr Marriner tapping on the table, his wife studying her rings. At last she said,

'They're all so class-conscious nowadays.'

'It wasn't that,' said Anne.

'What was it?'

Before she had time to answer—if she would have answered —the door opened and Jeremy came in, flushed and excited but also triumphant, with the triumph he had won over himself. He didn't go to his place but stood away from the table looking at his father.

'He wouldn't take it,' he said. 'He said it wasn't enough. He said you would know why.'

'I should know why?' Mr Marriner's frown was an effort to remember something. 'What sort of a man is he, Jeremy?'

'Tall and thin, with a pulled-in face.'

'And the boy?'

'He looked about seven. He was crying.'

'Is it anyone you know, Henry?' asked his wife.

'I was trying to think. Yes, no, well, yes, I might have known him.' Mr Marriner's agitation was now visible to them all, and even more felt than seen. 'What did you say, Jeremy?'

Jeremy's breast swelled.

'I told him to go away.'

'And has he gone?'

As though in answer the bell pealed again.

'I'll go this time,' said Mrs Marriner. 'Perhaps I can do something for the child.'

And she was gone before her husband's outstretched arm could stop her.

Again the trio sat in silence, the children less concerned with themselves than with the gleam that kept coming and going in their father's eyes like a dipping headlight.

Mrs Marriner came back much more self-possesed than either of her children had.

'I don't think he means any harm,' she said, 'he's a little cracked, that's all. We'd better humour him. He said he wanted to see you, Henry, but I told him you were out. He said that what we offered wasn't enough and that he wanted what you gave him last year, whatever that means. So I suggest we give him something that isn't money. Perhaps you could spare him one of your boxes, Jeremy. A Christmas box is quite a good idea.'

'He won't take it,' said Anne, before Jeremy could speak.

'Why not?'

'Because he can't,' said Anne.

'Can't? What do you mean?' Anne shook her head. Her mother didn't press her.

'Well, you are a funny girl,' she said. 'Anyhow, we can but try. Oh, and he said they'd sing us one more carol.'

They set themselves to listen, and in a moment the strains of 'God rest you merry, gentlemen' began.

Jeremy got up from the table.

'I don't believe they're singing the words right,' he said. He went to the window and opened it, letting in a puff of icy air.

'Oh, do shut it!'

'Just a moment. I want to make sure.'

They all listened, and this is what they heard.

> 'God blast the master of this house,
> Likewise the mistress too,
> And all the little children,
> That round the table go.'

Jeremy shut the window. 'Did you hear?' he croaked.

'I thought I did,' said Mrs Marriner. 'But it might have been "bless," the words sound so much alike. Henry, dear, don't look so serious.'

The door bell rang for the third time. Before the jangling died down, Mr Marriner rose shakily.

'No, no, Henry,' said his wife. 'Don't go, it'll only encourage them. Besides, I said you were out.' He looked at her doubtfully, and the bell rang again, louder than before. 'They'll soon get tired of it,' she said, 'if no one comes. Henry, I beg you not to go.' And when he still stared at her with groping eyes, she added:

'You can't remember how much you gave him last year?' Her husband made an impatient gesture with his hand.

'But if you go take one of Jeremy's boxes.'

'It isn't a box they want,' he said, 'it's a bullet.'

He went to the sideboard and brought out a pistol. It was an old-fashioned saloon pistol, a relic from the days when Henry's father, in common with others of his generation, had practised pistol-shooting, and it had lain at the back of a drawer in the sideboard longer than any of them could remember.

'No, Henry, no! You mustn't get excited! And think of the child!'

She was on her feet now; they all were.

'Stay where you are!' he snarled.

'Anne! Jeremy! Tell him not to! Try to stop him.' But his children could not in a moment shake off the obedience of a lifetime, and helplessly they watched him go.

'But it isn't any good, it isn't any good!' Anne kept repeating.

'What isn't any good, darling?'

'The pistol. You see, I've seen through him!'

'How do you mean, seen through him? Do you mean he's an imposter?'

'No, no. I've really seen through him.' Anne's voice sank to a whisper. 'I saw the street lamp shining through a hole in his head.'

'Darling, darling!'

'Yes, and the boy, too—'

'Will you be quiet, Anne?' cried Jeremy from behind the window curtain. 'Will you be quiet? They're saying something. Now Daddy's pointing the gun at him—he's got him covered! His finger's on the trigger, he's going to shoot! No, he isn't. The man's come nearer—he's come right up to Daddy! Now he's showing him something, something on his forehead—oh if I had a torch—and Daddy's dropped it, he's dropped the gun!'

As he spoke they heard the clatter; it was like the sound that gives confirmation to a wireless commentator's words. Jeremy's voice broke out again:

'He's going off with them—he's going off with them! They're leading him away!'

Before she or any of them could reach the door, Mrs Marriner had fainted.

. . .

The police didn't take long to come. On the grass near the garden gate they found the body. There were signs of a struggle —a slither, like a skid mark, on the gravel, heel marks dug deep into the turf. Later it was learnt that Mr Marriner had died of coronary thrombosis. Of his assailants not a trace was found. But the motive couldn't have been robbery, for all the coins he had had in his pockets, and all the notes out of his wallet, in fact all his available capital, lay scattered round him, as if he had made a last attempt to buy his captors off, but couldn't give them enough.

L. P. HARTLEY, 1895–

GHOST STORIES

All argument is against them, but all belief is for them.
SAMUEL JOHNSON, 1709–84

THE LEAF-SWEEPER

BEHIND the town hall there is a wooded parkland which, towards the end of November, begins to draw a thin blue cloud right into itself; and as a rule, the park floats in this haze until mid-February. I pass every day, and see Johnnie Geddes in the heart of the mist, sweeping up the leaves. Now and again he stops, and jerking his long head erect, looks indignantly at the pile of leaves, as if it ought not to be there; then he sweeps on. This business of leaf-sweeping, he learnt during the years he spent in the asylum; it was the job they always gave him to do; and when he was discharged the town council gave him the leaves to sweep. But the indignant movement of the head comes naturally to him, for this has been one of his habits since he was the most promising and buoyant and vociferous graduate of his year. He looks much older than he is, for it is not quite twenty years ago that Johnnie founded the Society for the Abolition of Christmas.

Johnnie was living with his aunt, then. I was at school, and in the Christmas holidays, Miss Geddes gave me her nephew's pamphlet, *How to Grow Rich at Christmas*. It sounded very likely, but it turned out that you grow rich at Christmas by doing away with Christmas, and so I pondered Johnnie's pamphlet no further.

But it was only his first attempt. He had, within the next three years, founded his society of Abolitionists. His new book, *Abolish Christmas Or We Die* was in great demand at the public library, and my turn for it came at last. Johnnie was really convincing, this time, and most people were completely won over until after they had closed the book. I got an old copy for sixpence the other day, and despite the lapse of time, it still proves conclusively that Christmas is a national crime. Johnnie demonstrates that every human-unit in the kingdom faces inevitable starvation within a period inversely proportionate to that in which one in every six industrial-productivity units, if you see what he means, stops producing toys wherewith to fill the stockings of the educational-intake-units. He cites appalling statistics to show that 1.024 percent of the time squandered each Christmas in reckless shopping and thoughtless churchgoing, brings the nation closer to its doom by five years. A few readers protested, but Johnnie was able to demolish their muddled arguments, and meanwhile the Society for the Abolition of Christmas increased. But Johnnie was troubled. Not only did Christmas rage throughout the kingdom as usual that year, but he had private information that many of the Society's members had broken the Oath of Abstention.

He decided, then, to strike at the very roots of Christmas. Johnnie gave up his job on the Drainage Supply Board; he gave up all his prospects and, financed by a few supporters, retreated for two years to study the roots of Christmas. Then, all jubilant, Johnnie produced his next and last book, in which he established, either that Christmas was an invention of the Early Fathers to propitiate the pagans, or it was invented by the pagans to placate the Early Fathers, I forget which. Against the advice of his friends, Johnnie entitled it *Christmas and Christianity*. It sold eighteen copies. Johnnie never really recovered from this; and it happened, about that time, that the girl he was engaged to, an ardent Abolitionist, sent him a pullover she had knitted, for Christmas; he sent it back, enclosing a copy of the Society's rules, and she sent back the ring. But in any case, during Johnnie's absence, the Society had been undermined by a moderate faction. These moderates finally became more moderate, and the whole thing broke up.

71

Soon after this, I left the district, and it was some years before I saw Johnnie again. One Sunday afternoon in summer, I was idling among the crowds who were gathered to hear the speakers at Hyde Park. One little crowd surrounded a man who bore a banner marked 'Crusade against Christmas'; his voice was frightening; it carried an unusually long way. This was Johnnie. A man in the crowd told me Johnnie was there every Sunday, very violent about Christmas, and that he would soon be taken up for insulting language. As I saw in the papers, he was soon taken up for insulting language. And a few months later I heard that poor Johnnie was in a mental home, because he had Christmas on the brain and couldn't stop shouting about it.

After that, I forgot all about him until, three years ago, in December, I went to live near the town where Johnnie had spent his youth. On the afternoon of Christmas Eve I was walking with a friend, noticing what had changed in my absence, and what hadn't. We passed a long large house, once famous for its armoury, and I saw that the iron gates were wide open.

'They used to be kept shut,' I said.

'That's an asylum now,' said my friend; 'they let the mild cases work in the grounds, and leave the gates open to give them a feeling of freedom.'

'But,' said my friend, 'they lock everything inside. Door after door. The lift as well; they keep it locked.'

While my friend was chattering, I stood in the gateway and looked in. Just beyond the gate was a great bare elm-tree. There I saw a man in brown corduroys, sweeping up the leaves. Poor soul, he was shouting about Christmas.

'That's Johnnie Geddes,' I said. 'Has he been there all these years?'

'Yes,' said my friend as we walked on; 'I believe he gets worse at this time of year.'

'Does his aunt see him?'

'Yes. And she sees nobody else.'

We were, in fact, approaching the house where Miss Geddes lived. I suggested we called on her. I had known her well.

'No fear,' said my friend.

I decided to go in, all the same, and my friend walked on to the town.

Miss Geddes had changed, more than the landscape. She had been a solemn, calm woman, and now she moved about quickly, and gave short agitated smiles. She took me to her sitting-room, and as she opened the door she called to someone inside,

'Johnnie, see who's come to see us!'

A man, dressed in a dark suit, was standing on a chair, fixing holly behind a picture. He jumped down.

'Happy Christmas,' he said. 'A Happy and a Merry Christmas indeed. I do hope,' he said, 'you're going to stay for tea as we've got a delightful Christmas cake, and at this season of goodwill I would be cheered indeed if you could see how charmingly it's decorated; it has "Happy Christmas" in red icing, and then there's a robin and—'

'Johnnie,' said Miss Geddes, 'you're forgetting the carols.'

'The carols,' he said. He lifted a gramophone record from a pile, and put it on. It was *The Holly and the Ivy*.

'It's *The Holly and the Ivy*,' said Miss Geddes. 'Can't we have something else? we had that all morning.'

'It is sublime,' he said, beaming from his chair, and holding up his hand for silence.

While Miss Geddes went to fetch the tea, and he sat absorbed in his carol, I watched him. He was so like Johnnie, that if I hadn't seen poor Johnnie a few moments before, sweeping up the asylum leaves, I would have thought he really was Johnnie. Miss Geddes returned with the tray, and while he rose to put on another record, he said something that startled me,

'I saw you in the crowd that Sunday when I was speaking at Hyde Park.'

'What a memory you have!' said Miss Geddes.

'It must be ten years ago,' he said.

'My nephew has altered his opinion of Christmas,' she explained. 'He always comes home for Christmas now, and don't we have a jolly time, Johnnie?'

'Rather!' he said; 'Oh, let me cut the cake.'

He was very excited about the cake. With a flourish he dug a large knife into the side. The knife slipped, and I saw it run deep into his finger. Miss Geddes did not move. He wrenched his finger away, and went on slicing the cake.

'Isn't it bleeding?' I said.

He held up his hand. I could see the deep cut, but there was no blood.

Deliberately, and perhaps desperately, I turned to Miss Geddes.

'That house up the road,' I said. 'I see it's a mental home now. I passed it this afternoon.'

'Johnnie,' said Miss Geddes, as one who knows the game is up; 'go and fetch the mince-pies.'

He went, whistling a carol.

'You passed the asylum,' said Miss Geddes wearily.

'Yes,' I said.

'And you saw Johnnie sweeping up the leaves.'

'Yes.'

We could still hear the whistling of the carol.

'Who is *he*?' I said.

'That's Johnnie's ghost,' she said. 'He comes home every Christmas.'

'But,' she said, 'I don't like him. I can't bear him any longer, and I'm going away tomorrow. I don't want Johnnie's ghost, I want Johnnie in flesh and blood.'

I shuddered, thinking of the cut finger that could not bleed. And I left, before Johnnie's ghost returned with the mince pies.

Next day, as I had arranged to join a family who lived in the town, I started walking over about noon. Because of the light mist, I didn't see, at first, who it was approaching. It was a man, waving his arm to me. It turned out to be Johnnie's ghost.

'Happy Christmas. What do you think,' said Johnnie's ghost, 'my aunt has gone to London. Fancy, on Christmas day, and I thought she was at church, and here I am without anyone to spend a jolly Christmas with, and of course I forgive her, as it's the season of goodwill, but I'm glad to see you, because now I can come with you, wherever it is you're going, and we can all have a Happy—'

'Go away,' I said, and walked on.

It sounds hard. But perhaps you don't know how repulsive and loathsome is the ghost of a living man. The ghosts of the dead may be all right, but the ghost of mad Johnnie gave me the creeps.

'Clear off,' I said.

He continued walking beside me. 'As it's the time of goodwill, I make allowances for your tone,' he said. 'But I'm coming.'

We had reached the asylum gates, and there, in the grounds, I saw Johnnie sweeping the leaves. I suppose it was his way of going on strike, working on Christmas day. He was making a noise about Christmas.

74

On a sudden impulse I said to Johnnie's ghost, 'You want company?'

'Certainly,' he replied; 'it's the season of—'

'Then you shall have it,' I said.

I stood in the gateway. 'Oh, Johnnie,' I called.

He looked up.

'I've brought your ghost to see you, Johnnie.'

'Well, well,' said Johnnie, advancing to meet his ghost. 'Just imagine it!'

'Happy Christmas,' said Johnnie's ghost.

'Oh, really?' said Johnnie.

I left them to it. And when I looked back, wondering if they would come to blows, I saw that Johnnie's ghost was sweeping the leaves as well. They seemed to be arguing at the same time. But it was still misty, and really, I can't say whether, when I looked a second time, there were two men or one man sweeping the leaves.

Johnnie began to improve in the New Year. At least, he stopped shouting about Christmas, and then he never mentioned it at all; in a few months, when he had almost stopped saying anything, they discharged him.

The town council gave him the leaves of the park to sweep. He seldom speaks, and recognizes nobody. I see him every day at the late end of the year, working within the mist. Sometimes, if there is a sudden gust, he jerks his head up to watch a few leaves falling behind him, as if amazed that they are undeniably there, although, by rights, the falling of leaves should be stopped.

MURIEL SPARK

CHRISTMAS EVE, 1012

THEY will be singing amorous Songs and Ditties (if yong especially), and cannot abstain though it be when they go to, or should be at Church. We have a pretty Story to this purpose in *Westmonasteriensis,* an old Writer of ours (if you will believe it). *An. Dom.* 1012, at *Colewiz* in *Saxony,* on *Christmass*-eve a company of yong Men and Maids, whilst the Priest was at Mass in the Church, were singing Catches and love songs in the

Church-yard, he sent to them to make less noise, but they sung on still, and if you will, you shall have the very Song it self.

> *Equitabat homo per sylvam frondosam,*
> *Ducebatque secum Meswinden formosam,*
> *Quid stamus, cur non imus?*

> A fellow rid by the green-wood side,
> And fair Meswinde was his bride,
> Why stand we so, and do not go?

This they sung, he chaft, till at length, impatient as he was, he prayed to S. *Magnus,* patron of the Church, they might all there sing and dance 'till that time Twelvemonth, and so they did, without Meat and Drink, wearisomness or giving over, till at Year's end they ceased singing, and were absolved by *Herebertus* Archbishop of *Colen.*

ROBERT BURTON, 1577–1640

CHRISTMAS EVE, 1768

I T being Christmas Eve we had the New Singers of C[astle] Cary this evening at Parsonage, and they having been at great expenses in learning to sing, my Father and myself gave them double what we used to do, and therefore instead of one shilling gave each 0.2.0.

JAMES WOODFORDE, 1740–1803

CHRISTMAS EVE, 1903

I C A M E to Burslem yesterday evening with Tertia and William and a headache. Went out this morning and saw numbers of people. Walking to Hanley this afternoon I was struck by the orange-apple *cold* Christmas smell of the greengrocers' shops.

ARNOLD BENNETT, 1867–1931

WHEN I WAS ELEVEN

Dec. 24th, 1771. Eder Whitwell told my aunt that this winter began as did the winter of 1740. How that was I don't remember but this I know that to-day is by far the coldest we have had since I have been in New England. (N.B. All run that are abroad.) Last Sabbath being rainy I went to & from meeting in Mr. Soley's chaise. I dined at unkle Winslow's the walking being so bad I rode there and back to meeting. Every drop that fell froze, so that yesterday morning to this time the appearance has been similar to the description I sent you last winter. The walking is so slippery & the air so cold, that aunt chuses to have me for her scoller these two days. And so to-morrow will be a holiday, so the pope and his associates have ordained, my aunt thinks not to trouble Mrs. Smith with me this week. I began a shift at home yesterday for myself, it is pretty forward. Last Saturday was seven-night my aunt Suky was delivered of a pretty little son, who was baptized by Dr. Cooper the next day by the name of Charles. I knew nothing of it till noonday, when I went there a-visiting. Last Thursday I din'd & spent the afternoon at unkle Joshua's, I should have gone to lecture with my aunt and heard Mr. Hunt preach, but she would not wait till I came from writing-school. Miss Atwood, the last of our boarders, went the same day. Miss Griswold & Miss Meriam, having departed some time agone. I forget whether I mention'd the recept of Nancy's present. I am obliged to her for it. The Dolphin is still whole. And like to remain so.

ANNA GREEN WINSLOW, 1759-79

WHEN I WAS FOURTEEN

24th December, 1903: Went out with L—— to try to see the squirrels again. We could not find one and were just wondering if we should draw blank when L—— noticed one clinging to the bark of a tree with a nut in its mouth. We gave it a good chase, but it escaped into the thickest part of the fir tree, still carrying the nut, and we gave up firing at it. Later on, L—— got foolishly mischievous—owing, I suppose, to our lack of sport— and unhinged a gate which he carried two yards into a copse, and threw it on the ground. Just then, he saw the Squirrel again and jumped over the hedge into the copse, chasing it from tree to tree with his catty. Having lost it, he climbed a fir tree into a Squirrel's drey at the top and sat there on the tree top, and I, below, was just going to lift the gate back when I looked up and saw a farmer watching me, menacing and silent. I promptly dropped the gate and fled. L—— from his Squirrel's drey, not knowing what had happened, called out to me about the nest—that there was nothing in it. The man looked up and asked him who he was and who I was. L—— would not say and would not come down. The farmer said he would come up. L—— answered that if he did he would 'gob' [i.e. spit] on him. Eventually L—— climbed down and asked the farmer for a glass of cider. The latter gave him his boot and L—— ran away.

W. N. P. BARBELLION, 1889–1919

THE THIEVES WHO COULDN'T HELP SNEEZING

MANY years ago, when oak trees now past their prime were about as large as elderly gentlemen's walking-sticks, there lived in Wessex a yeoman's son, whose name was Hubert. He was about fourteen years of age, and was as remarkable for his candour and lightness of heart as for his physical courage, of which, indeed, he was a little vain.

One cold Christmas Eve his father, having no other help at hand, sent him on an important errand to a small town several miles from home. He travelled on horseback, and was detained by the business till a late hour of the evening. At last, however, it was completed; he returned to the inn, the horse was saddled, and he started on his way. His journey homeward lay through the Vale of Blackmore, a fertile but somewhat lonely district, with heavy clay roads and crooked lanes. In those days, too, a great part of it was thickly wooded.

It must have been about nine o'clock when, riding along amid the overhanging trees upon his stout-legged cob, Jerry, and singing a Christmas carol, to be in harmony with the season, Hubert fancied that he heard a noise among the boughs. This recalled to his mind that the spot he was traversing bore an evil name. Men had been waylaid there. He looked at Jerry, and wished he had been of any other colour than light grey; for on this account the docile animal's form was visible even here in the dense shade. 'What do I care?' he said aloud, after a few minutes of reflection. 'Jerry's legs are too nimble to allow any highwayman to come near me.'

'Ha! ha! indeed,' was said in a deep voice; and the next moment a man darted from the thicket on his right hand, another man from the thicket on his left hand, and another from a tree-trunk a few yards ahead. Hubert's bridle was seized, he was pulled from his horse, and although he struck out with all his might, as a brave boy would naturally do, he was over-powered. His arms were tied behind him, his legs bound tightly together, and he was thrown into a ditch. The robbers, whose faces he could now dimly perceive to be artificially blackened, at once departed, leading off the horse.

As soon as Hubert had a little recovered himself, he found that by great exertion he was able to extricate his legs from the cord; but, in spite of every endeavour, his arms remained bound as fast as before. All, therefore, that he could do was to rise to his feet and proceed on his way with his arms behind him, and trust to chance for getting them unfastened. He knew that it would be impossible to reach home on foot that night, and in such a con-dition; but he walked on. Owing to the confusion which this attack caused in his brain, he lost his way, and would have been inclined to lie down and rest till morning among the dead leaves had he not known the danger of sleeping without wrappers in a frost so severe. So he wandered farther onwards, his arms wrung and numbed by the cord which pinioned him, and his heart aching for the loss of poor Jerry, who never had been known to kick, or bite, or show a single vicious habit. He was not a little glad when he discerned through the trees a distant light. Towards this he made his way, and presently found himself in front of a large mansion with flanking wings, gables, and towers, the battlements and chimneys showing their shapes against the stars.

All was silent; but the door stood wide open, it being from this door that the light shone which had attracted him. On enter-ing he found himself in a vast apartment arranged as a dining-hall, and brilliantly illuminated. The walls were covered with a great deal of dark wainscoting, formed into moulded panels, carvings, closet-doors, and the usual fittings of a house of that kind. But what drew his attention most was the large table in the midst of the hall, upon which was spread a sumptuous supper, as yet untouched. Chairs were placed around, and it appeared as if something had occurred to interrupt the meal just at the time when all were ready to begin.

Even had Hubert been so inclined, he could not have eaten in his helpless state, unless by dipping his mouth into the dishes, like a pig or cow. He wished first to obtain assistance; and was about to penetrate farther into the house for that purpose when he heard hasty footsteps in the porch and the words, 'Be quick!' uttered in the deep voice which had reached him when he was dragged from the horse. There was only just time for him to dart under the table before three men entered the dining-hall. Peeping from beneath the hanging edges of the tablecloth, he perceived that their faces, too, were blackened, which at once removed any doubts he may have felt that these were the same thieves.

'Now, then,' said the first—the man with the deep voice— 'let us hide ourselves. They will all be back again in a minute. That was a good trick to get them out of the house—eh?'

'Yes. You well imitated the cries of a man in distress,' said the second.

'Excellently,' said the third.

'But they will soon find out that it was a false alarm. Come, where shall we hide? It must be some place we can stay in for two or three hours, till all are in bed and asleep. Ah! I have it. Come this way! I have learnt that the farther cupboard is not opened once in a twelvemonth; it will serve our purpose exactly.'

The speaker advanced into a corridor which led from the hall. Creeping a little farther forward, Hubert could discern that the cupboard stood at the end, facing the dining-hall. The thieves entered it, and closed the door. Hardly breathing, Hubert glided forward to learn a little more of their intention, if possible; and, coming close, he could hear the robbers whispering about the different rooms where the jewels, plate, and other valuables of the house were kept, which they plainly meant to steal.

They had not been long in hiding when a gay chattering of ladies and gentlemen was audible on the terrace without. Hubert felt that it would not do to be caught prowling about the house, unless he wished to be taken for a robber himself; and he slipped softly back to the hall, out at the door, and stood in a dark corner

of the porch, where he could see everything without being himself seen. In a moment or two a whole troop of personages came gliding past him into the house. There were an elderly gentleman and lady, eight or nine young ladies, as many young men, besides half a dozen menservants and maids. The mansion had apparently been quite emptied of its occupants.

'Now, children and young people, we will resume our meal,' said the old gentleman. 'What the noise could have been I cannot understand. I never felt so certain in my life that there was a person being murdered outside my door.'

Then the ladies began saying how frightened they had been, and how they had expected an adventure, and how it had ended in nothing after all.

'Wait a while,' said Hubert to himself. 'You'll have adventure enough by-and-by, ladies.'

It appeared that the young men and women were married sons and daughters of the old couple, who had come that day to spend Christmas with their parents.

The door was then closed, Hubert being left outside in the porch. He thought this a proper moment for asking their assistance; and, since he was unable to knock with his hands, began boldly to kick the door.

'Hullo! What disturbance are you making here?' said a footman who opened it; and, seizing Hubert by the shoulder, he pulled him into the dining-hall. 'Here's a strange boy I have found making a noise in the porch, Sir Simon.'

Everybody turned.

'Bring him forward,' said Sir Simon, the old gentleman before mentioned. 'What are you doing there, my boy?'

'Why his arms are tied!' said one of the ladies.

'Poor fellow!' said another.

Hubert at once began to explain that he had been waylaid on his journey home, robbed of his horse, and mercilessly left in this condition by the thieves.

'Only to think of it!' exclaimed Sir Simon.

'That's a likely story,' said one of the gentleman-guests, incredulously.

'Doubtful, hey?' asked Sir Simon.

'Perhaps he's a robber himself,' suggested a lady.

'There is a curiously wild wicked look about him, certainly, now that I examine him closely,' said the old mother.

81

Hubert blushed with shame; and, instead of continuing his story, and relating that robbers were concealed in the house, he doggedly held his tongue, and half resolved to let them find out their danger for themselves.

'Well, untie him,' said Sir Simon. 'Come, since it is Christmas Eve, we'll treat him well. Here, my lad; sit down in that empty seat at the bottom of the table, and make as good a meal as you can. When you have had your fill we will listen to more particulars of your story.'

The feast then proceeded; and Hubert, now at liberty, was not at all sorry to join in. The more they ate and drank the merrier did the company become; the wine flowed freely, the logs flared up the chimney, the ladies laughed at the gentlemen's stories; in short, all went as noisily and as happily as a Christmas gathering in old times possibly could do.

Hubert, in spite of his hurt feelings at their doubts of his honesty, could not help being warmed both in mind and in body by the good cheer, the scene, and the example of hilarity set by his neighbours. At last he laughed as heartily at their stories and repartees as the old Baronet, Sir Simon, himself. When the meal was almost over, one of the sons, who had drunk a little too much wine, after the manner of men in that century, said to Hubert, 'Well, my boy, how are you? Can you take a pinch of snuff?' He held out one of the snuff-boxes which were then becoming common among young and old throughout the country.

'Thank you,' said Hubert, accepting a pinch.

'Tell the ladies who you are, what you are made of, and what you can do,' the young man continued, slapping Hubert upon the shoulder.

'Certainly,' said our hero, drawing himself up, and thinking it best to put a bold face on the matter. 'I am a travelling magician.'

'Indeed!'

'What shall we hear next?'

'Can you call up spirits from the vasty deep, young wizard?'

'I can conjure up a tempest in a cupboard,' Hubert replied.

'Ha-ha!' said the old Baronet, pleasantly rubbing his hands. 'We must see this performance. Girls, don't go away: here's something to be seen.'

'Not dangerous, I hope?' said the old lady.

Hubert rose from the table. 'Hand me your snuff-box, please,' he said to the young man who had made free with him. 'And now,' he continued, 'without the least noise, follow me. If any of you speak it will break the spell.'

They promised obedience. He entered the corridor, and, taking off his shoes, went on tiptoe to the cupboard door, the guests advancing in a silent group at a little distance behind him. Hubert next placed a stool in front of the door, and, by standing upon it, was tall enough to reach the top. He then, just as noiselessly, poured all the snuff from the box along the upper edge of the door, and, with a few short puffs of breath, blew the snuff through the chink into the interior of the cupboard. He held up his finger to the assembly, that they might be silent.

'Dear me, what's that?' said the old lady, after a minute or two had elapsed.

A suppressed sneeze had come from inside the cupboard.

Hubert held up his finger again.

'How very singular,' whispered Sir Simon. 'This is most interesting.'

Hubert took advantage of the moment to gently slide the bolt of the cupboard door into its place. 'More snuff,' he said, calmly.

'More snuff,' said Sir Simon. Two or three gentlemen passed their boxes, and the contents were blown in at the top of the cupboard. Another sneeze, not quite so well suppressed as the first, was heard : then another, which seemed to say that it would not be suppressed under any circumstances whatever. At length there arose a perfect storm of sneezes.

'Excellent, excellent for one so young!' said Sir Simon. 'I am much interested in this trick of throwing the voice—called, I believe, ventriloquism.'

'More snuff,' said Hubert.

'More snuff,' said Sir Simon. Sir Simon's man brought a large jar of the best scented Scotch.

Hubert once more charged the upper chink of the cupboard, and blew the snuff into the interior, as before. Again he charged, and again, emptying the whole contents of the jar. The tumult of sneezes became really extraordinary to listen to—there was no cessation. It was like wind, rain, and sea battling in a hurricane.

'I believe there are men inside, and that it is no trick at all!' exclaimed Sir Simon, the truth flashing on him.

'There are,' said Hubert. 'They are come to rob the house; and they are the same who stole my horse.'

The sneezes changed to spasmodic groans. One of the thieves, hearing Hubert's voice, cried, 'Oh! mercy! mercy! let us out of this!'

'Where's my horse?' cried Hubert.

'Tied to a tree in the hollow behind Short's Gibbet. Mercy! mercy! let us out, or we shall die of suffocation!'

All the Christmas guests now perceived that this was no longer sport, but serious earnest. Guns and cudgels were procured; all the menservants were called in, and arranged in position outside the cupboard. At a signal Hubert withdrew the bolt, and stood on the defensive. But the three robbers, far from attacking them, were found crouching in the corner, gasping for breath. They made no resistance; and, being pinioned, were placed in an out-house till the morning.

Hubert now gave the remainder of his story to the assembled company, and was profusely thanked for the services he had rendered. Sir Simon pressed him to stay over the night, and accept the use of the best bedroom the house afforded, which had been occupied by Queen Elizabeth and King Charles successively when on their visits to this part of the country. But Hubert declined, being anxious to find his horse Jerry, and to test the truth of the robbers' statements concerning him.

Several of the guests accompanied Hubert to the spot behind the gibbet, alluded to by the thieves as where Jerry was hidden. When they reached the knoll and looked over, behold! there the horse stood, uninjured, and quite unconcerned. At sight of Hubert he neighed joyfully; and nothing could exceed Hubert's gladness at finding him. He mounted, wished his friends 'Good-night!' and cantered off in the direction they pointed out, reaching home safely about four o'clock in the morning.

THOMAS HARDY, 1840–1928

IT was years ago, I remember, one Christmas Eve when I was dining with friends: a lady beside me made in the course of talk one of those allusions that I have always found myself recognizing on the spot as 'germs.' The germ, wherever gathered, has ever been for me the germ of a 'story,' and most of the stories straining to shape under my hand have sprung from a single small seed, a seed as minute and wind-blown as that casual hint for *The Spoils of Poynton* dropped unwittingly by my neighbour, a mere floating particle in the stream of talk. What above all comes back to me with this reminiscence is the sense of the inveterate minuteness, on such happy occasions, of the previous particle—reduced, that is, to its mere fruitful essence. Such is the interesting truth about the stray suggestion, the wandering word, the vague echo, at touch of which the novelist's imagination winces as at the prick of some sharp point: its virtue is all in its needle-like quality, the power to penetrate as finely as possible. This fineness it is that communicates the virus of suggestion, anything more than the minimum of which spoils the operation. . . .

So it was, at any rate, that when my amiable friend, on the Christmas Eve, before the table that glowed safe and fair through the brown London night, spoke of such an odd matter as that a good lady in the north, always well looked on, was at daggers drawn with her only son, ever hitherto exemplary, over the ownership of the valuable furniture of a fine old house just accruing to the young man by his father's death, I instantly became aware, with my 'sense for the subject,' of the prick of inoculation; the *whole* of the virus, as I have called it, being infused by that single touch. For the action taken, and on which my friend, as I knew she would, had already begun all complacently and benightedly further to report, I had absolutely, and could have, no scrap of use; one had been so perfectly qualified to say in advance, 'It's the perfect little workable thing, but she'll strangle it in the cradle, even while she pretends, all so cheeringly, to rock it; wherefore I'll stay her hand while yet there's time.' I didn't of course stay her hand—there never *is* in such cases 'time'; and I had once more the full demonstration of the fatal futility of Fact. The turn taken by the excellent situation—excellent, for development, if arrested in the right place, that is in the germ—had the full measure of the classic ineptitude; to which with the full measure of the artistic irony one could once more, and for the thousandth time, but take off one's hat. It was not, however, that this in the least mattered, once the seed had been transplanted to richer soil; and I dwell on that almost inveterate redundancy of the wrong, as opposed to the ideal right, in any free flowering of the actual, by reason only of its approach to calculable regularity.

If there was nothing regular meanwhile. . . .

HENRY JAMES, 1843–1916

HUGH WALPOLE IN HOLLYWOOD, 1935

HUGH was encouraged by the excellent news of *The Inquisitor* at home, where the book was being listed as the most popular novel of the season. He was also pleased when he was once more entrusted with the scenario of *Kim,* for which another writer had prepared a first draft. As Christmas approached, his thoughts went back to the other Christmases he had spent in America: few of them had come up to his expectations, but this one he felt sure would be different. He was right. The attractive American custom of setting up in the streets large Christmas trees covered with brightly-coloured lights was, as might be expected, in Hollywood carried to extremes. The whole brittle artificial city glittered gaily every night, and Hugh had to confess that he loved it. To drive down Hollywood Boulevard, he said, took one's breath away.

He stayed at Jean Hersholt's Christmas Eve party until three o'clock on Christmas morning, and as he drove home the stars were competing with the Christmas trees. Later he went to church and 'found it gay with poinsettias and a lady choir in red caps looking like Roman senators.' The midday party was at the Boleslawsky's, where Hugh received any amount of presents and admired the new baby, the latest in his long string

of godchildren. An evening party at George Cukor's brought to an end the happiest Christmas he had ever spent away from home, and when he came to wind up his diary for the year he could write himself down as 'very happy, quieter, less nervous, everyone more friendly. God be thanked!'

RUPERT HART-DAVIS, 1907–

DULCE DOMUM

A T last the Rat succeeded in decoying him to the table, and had just got seriously to work with the sardine-opener when sounds were heard from the fore-court without—sounds like the scuffling of small feet in the gravel and a confused murmur of tiny voices, while broken sentences reached them—'Now, all in a line —hold the lantern up a bit, Tommy—clear your throats first— no coughing after I say one, two, three.—Where's young Bill?— Here, come on, do, we're all a-waiting—'

'What's up?' inquired the Rat, pausing in his labours.

'I think it must be the field-mice,' replied the Mole, with a touch of pride in his manner. 'They go round carol-singing regularly at this time of the year. They're quite an institution in these parts. And they never pass me over—they come to Mole End last of all; and I used to give them hot drinks, and supper too sometimes, when I could afford it. It will be like old times to hear them again.'

'Let's have a look at them!' cried the Rat, jumping up and running to the door.

It was a pretty sight, and a seasonable one, that met their eyes when they flung the door open. In the fore-court, lit by the dim rays of a horn lantern, some eight or ten little field-mice stood in a semicircle, red worsted comforters round their throats, their fore-paws thrust deep into their pockets, their feet jigging for warmth. With bright beady eyes they glanced shyly at each other, sniggering a little, sniffing and applying coat-sleeves a good deal. As the door opened, one of the elder ones that carried the lantern was just saying, 'Now then, one, two, three!' and forthwith their shrill little voices uprose on the air, singing one of the old-time carols that their forefathers composed in fields that were fallow and held by frost, or when snow-bound in chimney corners, and handed down to be sung in the miry street to lamp-lit windows at Yule-time.

Villagers all, this frosty tide,
Let your doors swing open wide,
Though wind may follow, and snow beside,
Yet draw us in by your fire to bide;
    Joy shall be yours in the morning!

Here we stand in the cold and the sleet,
Blowing fingers and stamping feet,
Come from far away you to greet—
You by the fire and we in the street—
    Bidding you joy in the morning!

For ere one half of the night was gone,
Sudden a star has led us on,
Raining bliss and benison—
Bliss to-morrow and more anon,
    Joy for every morning!

Goodman Joseph toiled through the snow—
Saw the star o'er a stable low;
Mary she might not further go—
Welcome thatch, and litter below!
    Joy was hers in the morning!

And then they heard the angels tell
'Who were the first to cry Nowell?
Animals all, as it befell,
In the stable where they did dwell!
    Joy shall be theirs in the morning!'

The voices ceased, the singers, bashful, but smiling, exchanged
sidelong glances, and silence succeeded—but for a moment only.
Then, from up above and far away, down the tunnel they had
so lately travelled was borne to their ears in a faint musical hum
the sound of distant bells ringing a joyful and clangorous peal.

'Very well sung, boys!' cried the Rat heartily. 'And now come
along in, all of you, and warm yourselves by the fire, and have
something hot!'

'Yes, come along, field-mice,' cried the Mole eagerly. 'This is
quite like old times! Shut the door after you. Pull up that settle
to the fire. Now, you just wait a minute, while we— O, Ratty!'

he cried in despair, plumping down on a seat, with tears impending 'Whatever are we doing? We've nothing to give them!'

'You leave all that to me,' said the masterful Rat. 'Here, you with the lantern! Come over this way. I want to talk to you. Now, tell me, are there any shops open at this hour of the night?'

'Why, certainly, sir,' replied the field-mouse respectfully. 'At this time of the year our shops keep open to all sorts of hours.'

'Then look here!' said the Rat. 'You go off at once, you and your lantern, and you get me—'

Here much muttered conversation ensued, and the Mole only heard bits of it, such as—'Fresh, mind!—no, a pound of that will do—see you get Buggins's, for I won't have any other—no, only best—if you can't get it there, try somewhere else—yes, of course, home-made, no tinned stuff—well then, do the best you can!' Finally, there was a chink of coin passing from paw to paw, the field-mouse was provided with an ample basket for his purchases, and off he hurried, he and his lantern.

The rest of the field-mice, perched in a row on the settle, their small legs swinging, gave themselves up to enjoyment of the fire, and toasted their chilblains till they tingled; while the Mole, failing to draw them into easy conversation, plunged into family history and made each of them recite the names of his numerous brothers, who were too young, it appeared, to be allowed to go out a-carolling this year, but looked forward very shortly to winning the parental consent.

The Rat, meanwhile, was busy examining the label on one of the beer-bottles. 'I perceive this to be Old Burton,' he remarked approvingly. *'Sensible* Mole! The very thing! Now we shall be able to mull some ale! Get the things ready, Mole, while I draw the corks.'

It did not take long to prepare the brew and thrust the tin heater well into the heart of the fire; and soon every field-mouse was sipping and coughing and choking (for a little mulled ale goes a long way) and wiping his eyes and laughing and forgetting he had ever been cold in all his life.

'They act plays too, these fellows,' the Mole explained to the Rat. 'Make them up all by themselves, and act them afterwards. And very well they do it, too! They gave us a capital one last year, about a field-mouse who was captured at sea by a Barbary corsair, and made to row in a galley; and when he escaped and got home again, his lady-love had gone into a convent. Here, *you!* You were in it, I remember. Get up and recite a bit.'

The field-mouse addressed got up on his legs, giggled shyly, looked around the room, and remained absolutely tongue-tied. His comrades cheered him on, Mole coaxed and encouraged him, and the Rat went so far as to take him by the shoulders and shake him; but nothing could overcome his stage-fright. They were all busily engaged on him like watermen applying the Royal Humane Society's regulations to a case of long submersion, when the latch clicked, the door opened, and the field-mouse with the lantern reappeared, staggering under the weight of his basket.

There was no more talk of play-acting once the very real and solid contents of the basket had been tumbled out on the table. Under the generalship of Rat, everybody was set to do something or to fetch something. In a very few minutes supper was ready, and Mole, as he took the head of the table in a sort of dream, saw a lately barren board set thick with savoury comforts; saw his little friends' faces brighten and beam as they fell to without delay; and then let himself loose—for he was famished indeed—on the provender so magically provided, thinking what a happy home-coming this had turned out, after all. As they ate, they talked of old times, and the field-mice gave him the local gossip up to date, and answered as well as they could the hundred questions he had to ask them. The Rat said little or nothing, only taking care that each guest had what he wanted, and plenty of it, and that Mole had no trouble or anxiety about anything.

KENNETH GRAHAME, 1859–1932

'COME OVER, TOMMY! WE WON'T FIRE'

ON Christmas Eve of 1914 we were in the support line, about two hundred yards inside Ploegsteert Wood. It was freezing. Our overcoats were stiff as boards, our boots were too hard to remove, but we rejoiced. The mud was hard too! Also, happy thought, we would be able to *sleep* that night—inside a new blockhouse of oak-boughs and sandbags called Piccadilly Hotel. No bed but the cold earth, no blankets even; but sleep. Sleep!

Then came a message from brigade headquarters, brought, I think, by Second-Lieutenant Bruce Bairnsfather of the Warwicks. Wiring parties were required in no-man's-land all night. And there would be a moon. We would have to work only fifty yards from the German machine-guns in the White House opposite the eastern edge of the wood.

Two hours later, we filed out of the dark trees, into the naked moonlit terror of no-man's-land, holding shovels beside our faces, in hope of protection against the expected mortblast. The moon was high and white among frozen cloudlets. We were visible. Someone slipped, with a clank of spade or rifle. We flung ourselves on our faces. We waited. The battlefield was silent as the moon.

For an hour we worked in silence, in a most mysterious soundlessness. What had happened? We began to talk naturally as we drove in stakes, and pulled out concertinas of prepared wire. There was no rifle-fire either up or down the line, from way up north beyond Ypres to south beyond Armentières and the French Army. At midnight we were laughing as we worked. We heard singing from the German lines—carols the tunes of which we knew. I noticed a very bright light on a tall pole, raised in their lines. Down opposite the East Lancs trench, in front of the convent, a Christmas tree, with lighted candles, was set on their parapet. The unreal moonlight life went on, happily. Cries of 'Come over, Tommy! We won't fire at you!'

A dark figure approached me, hesitatingly. A trap? I walked towards it, with bumping heart. 'Merry Christmas, English friend!' We shook hands, tremulously. Then I saw that the light on the pole was the Morning Star, the Star in the East. It was Christmas morning.

All Christmas Day grey and khaki figures mingled and talked in no-man's-land. Picks and spades rang in the hard ground. It was strange to stare at the dead we had only glimpsed, swiftly, from the trenches. The shallowest graves were dug, filled, and set with crosses knocked together from lengths of ration-box wood, marked with indelible pencil. 'For King and Country.' 'Für Vaterland und Freiheit.'

Fatherland and Freedom! *Freedom?* How was this? *We* were fighting for freedom, our cause was just, we were defending Belgium, civilization . . . these fellows in grey were good fellows, they were—strangely—just men like ourselves. 'How can we lose the war, English comrade? Our cause is just, we are ringed with enemies who would crush us economically, we asked only for a place in the sun, and now we are defending our parents, our homes, our German soil. No, we cannot lose the war—for Right is on our side.' A most shaking, staggering thought: that both sides thought they were fighting for the same cause! The war was a terrible mistake! People at home did not know this! Then the Idea came to the young and callow soldier, that if only he could tell them all at home *what was really happening,* and if the German soldiers told their people the truth about us, the war would be over. But he hardly dared to think it, even to himself.

The next day was quiet, and the next. Waving hands from the trenches by day; singing and reflected blaze of trench bon-fires at night. It was a lovely time. On the third afternoon came a message from the Germans. 'At midnight our staff officers visit, and we must fire our automatic *pistolen,* but we will fire high, nevertheless please keep under cover.' At 11 p.m.—Berlin midnight—we saw the flashes going away into the air.

Two days later, an Army Order came from G.H.Q. to the effect that men found fraternizing with the enemy would be court-martialled, and if found guilty, would suffer the death penalty. And again in that place the Very lights soared over no-man's-land at night, and bullets cut showers of splinters from the trees, and sometimes, human flesh and bone.

HENRY WILLIAMSON, 1895–

ON THE WESTERN FRONT

... On
this night, when I was a young man in France, in Gallia Belgica,
the forward ballista-teams of the Island of Britain green-
garlanded their silent three-o-threes for this I saw and heard
their cockney song salute the happy morning; and later, on this
same morning certain of the footmen of Britain, walking in day-
light, upright, through the lanes of the war-net to outside and
beyond the rusted tip-belt, some with gifts, none with ported
weapons, embraced him between his *fossa* and ours, exchanging
tokens.

And this I know,
if only from immediate hearsay, for we had come on this mild
morning (it was a Green Christmas) back into the rear, two to
three thousand paces behind where his front *vallum* was called
by us, the Maiden's Bulge, and ours, the Pontiff's Neb, between
which parallels, these things, according to oral report reaching
us in this forward reserve area, were done,

BECAUSE OF THE CHILD
DAVID JONES, 1895–

CHRISTMAS EVE UNDER HOOKER'S STATUE

Tonight a blackout. Twenty years ago
I hung my stocking on the tree, and hell's
Serpent entwined the apple in the toe
To sting the child with knowledge. Hooker's heels
Kicking at nothing in the shifting snow,
A cannon and a cairn of cannon balls
Rusting before the blackened Statehouse, know
How the long horn of plenty broke like glass
In Hooker's gauntlets. Once I came from Mass;

Now storm-clouds shelter Christmas, once again
Mars meets his fruitless star with open arms,
His heavy sabre flashes with the rime,
The war-god's bronzed and empty forehead forms
Anonymous machinery from raw men;
The cannon on the Common cannot stun
The blundering butcher as he rides on Time—
The barrel clinks with holly. I am cold:
I ask for bread, my father gives me mould;

93

His stocking is full of stones. Santa in red
Is crowned with wizened berries. Man of war,
Where is the summer's garden? In its bed
The ancient speckled serpent will appear,
And black-eyed susan with her frizzled head.
When Chancellorsville mowed down the volunteer,
'All wars are boyish,' Herman Melville said;
But we are old, our fields are running wild :
Till Christ again turn wanderer and child.

ROBERT LOWELL, 1917–

'DEAREST MOTHER . . .'

Dec. 24th, 1866

DEAREST MOTHER, I got Jeff's letter sending the money toward the soldiers' dinner—it was more than I asked for, & was very good of them all—I have not had any trouble myself worth mentioning—the dinner has been got up at my instigation—I have contributed handsomely—but they (the Hospital steward &c.) have done the work.

Mother I sent Han a handsome little volume of Florence Percy's Poems, & $5 for a Christmas present. Sent it to-day— Poor Han—I suppose every such thing does her so much good—

Don't you believe that fool Heyde lately wrote a long letter to Mr. Raymond, editor of the N.Y. *Times*—in it he said 'Walt was a good fellow *enough—but*'—& then he went on to run down *Leaves of Grass*, like the rest of 'em—The way I know is Wm. O'Connor was invited by Raymond to come & see him— & he told O'Connor he had received a number of letters about that piece in the *Times* of Dec. 2, which I sent you. He said they all praised the piece, & thanked him (Raymond) for printing it, except one he got from a fellow in Vermont who called himself Walt Whitman's relation—a brother-in-law, he believed —quite a good deal of stuff. Raymond seemed to think the man was either crazy or a fool, & he treated the letter with contempt.—I don't want you to write any thing about it to Han, of course—only if she was here we would tell her. The puppy thought I suppose that he could get his letter printed, & injure me & my book—

We are likely to have a pleasant day for Christmas—when

94

I next write I will tell you about the dinner—I must inform you that I have had a present of a beautiful knife, a real Rogers steel, to-day from the Attorney-General—Mother $2 is for Nance —you can give it to her in money, or in any way you like.

Well, dear mother, this is Christmas eve, & I am writing it in the office by gas light, so as it will be ready to go to-morrow— I have not heard since from Mrs. Grayson.—Good night mother dear.

WALT WHITMAN, 1819–92

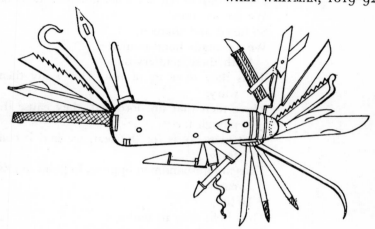

A BRIEF PROLOGUE

BIRTH, death, and copulation; redemption, farce, and horse-play—all these were a part of the mediæval drama of life as witness the *Wakefield Shepherds' Second Play.* . . .

PATRICK BELLAIRS, 1923–

THE WAKEFIELD SHEPHERDS' SECOND PLAY

First Shepherd: Lord! what, these weathers are cold, and I am ill happed;
I am near numb of hand, so long have I napped;
My legs bend and fold, my fingers are chapped,
It is not as I would, for I am all lapped
In sorrow.

95

In storms and tempest,
Now in the east, now in the west,
Woe is him has never rest,
  Mid day nor morrow.
But we silly shepherds, that walk upon the
    moor,
In faith, we are near hands out of the door;
No wonder, as it stands, if we be poor,
For the tilth of our lands lies fallow as the floor,
We are so lamed,
So taxed and shamed,
We are made hand-tamed,
  With these gentlery-men.
Thus they rieve us of rest, Our Lady them
    wary,
These men that are lord-tied, they cause the
    plough tarry.
That men say is for the best, we find it con-
    trary,
Thus are husbandmen opprest, in point to mis-
    carry,
  In life.
Thus hold they us under,
Thus they bring us in blunder,
It were great wonder,
  And ever should we thrive.
For may he get a painted sleeve, or a brooch
    now on days,
Woe is he that shall grieve, or once again says,
Dare no man him reprieve, what mast'ry he
    has,
And yet may none believe one word that he
    says—
  No letter.
He can make purveyance,
With boast and bragging,
And all through maintenance,
  Of men that are greater.
There shall come a swain, as proud as a pea-
    cock,
He must borrow my wain, my plough also,

Then I am full fain to grant or he go.
Thus live we in pain, anger, and woe,
　　By night and day ;
He must have if he longéd
If I should forego it,
I were better be hanged
　　Than once say him nay.
It does me good, as I walk thus by mine own,
Of this world for to talk in manner of moan
To my sheep will I stalk and hearken anon
There abide on a balk, or sit on a stone
　　Full soon.
For I trow, pardie !
True men if they be,
We get more company
　　Or it be noon.

Second Shepherd : *Benedicite* and *Dominus!* what may this be-
　　　　　　mean ?
　　　　　Why fares this world thus, oft have we not
　　　　　　seen.
　　　　　Lord, these weathers are spiteful, and the
　　　　　　weather full keen ;
　　　　　And the frost so hideous they water mine een,
　　　　　　No lie.
　　　　　Now in dry, now in wet,
　　　　　Now in snow, now in sleet,
　　　　　When my shoon freeze to my feet
　　　　　　It is not all easy.
　　　　　But as far as I ken, or yet as I go,
　　　　　We silly wedded men suffer much woe ;
　　　　　We have sorrow then and then, it falls often so,
　　　　　Silly Capyl, our hen, both to and fro
　　　　　　She cackles,
　　　　　But begin she to croak,
　　　　　To groan or to cluck,
　　　　　Woe is him, say of our cock,
　　　　　　For he is in the shackles.
　　　　　These men that are wed, have not all their will,
　　　　　When they are full hard placed, they sigh full
　　　　　　still ;
　　　　　God wait they are led full hard and full ill,

97

In bower nor in bed they say not there till
  This tide.
My part have I found,
My lesson is learn'd,
Woe is him that is bound,
  For he must abide.
But now late in our lives, a marvel to me,
That I think my heart riven, such wonders to
  see,
What that destiny drives it should so be,
Some men will have two wives, and some men
  three,
  In store.
Some are woe that have any;
But so far ken I,
Woe is he who has many,
  For he feels it sore.
But young men of wooing, for God that you
  bought,
Be well ware of wedding, and think in your
  thought
'Had I wist' is a thing it serves ye of nought
Mickle still mourning has wedding home
  brought,
  And griefs,
With many a sharp shower,
For thou may catch in an hour
That shall serve thee full sour
  As long as thou lives.
For as read I epistle, I have one to my fear
As sharp as a thistle, as rough as a briar.
She is browed like a bristle with a sour lenten
  cheer;
Had she once wet her whistle she could sing
  full clear
  Her pater-noster.
She is as great as a whale,
She has a gallon of gall;
By him that died for us all!
  I would I had run till I lost her.

First Shepherd: God look over the row, full deafly ye stand.

Second Shepherd: Yea, the devil in thy maw!—so tarrying,
     Saw thou aught now of Daw?
First Shepherd: Fir, on a lea land
     Heard I him blow, he comes here at hand,
      Not far;
     Stand still.
Second Shepherd: Why?
First Shepherd: For he comes here, hope I.
Second Shepherd: He will make us both a lie,
     But if we beware.
Third Shepherd: Christ's cross me speed, and Saint Nicholas!
     Thereof had I need, it is worse than it was.
     Whoso could take heed, and let the world pass,
     It is ever in dread and brittle as glass,
      And slithers,
     This world fared never so,
     With marvels mo and mo,
     Now in weal, now in woe,
      And all things withers.
     Was never since Noah's flood such floods seen,
     Winds and rains so rude, and storms so keen,
     Some stammered, some stood in doubt, as I
      ween,
     Now God turn all to good, I say as I mean,
      For ponder.
     These floods so they drown
     Both in fields and in town,
     They bear all down,
      And that is a wonder.
     We that walk in the nights, our cattle to keep,
     We see sudden sights, when other men sleep:
     Yet methinks my heart lights, I see shrews peep,
     Ye are two, all wights, I will give my sheep
      A turn.
     But full ill have I meant,
     As I walk on this field,
     I may lightly repent,
      My toes if I spurn.
     Ah, sir, God you save, and master mine!
     A drink fain would I have and somewhat to
      dine.

First Shepherd :	Christ's curs, my knave, thou art a lazy hind !
Second Shepherd :	What, the boy list rave. Abide until syne
	We have made it.
	I'll thrift on thy pate !
	Though the shrew came late
	Yet is he in state
	To dine if he had it.
Third Shepherd :	Such servants as I, that sweats and swinks,
	Eats my bread full dry, and that me forthinks ;
	We are oft wet and weary when master men
	winks,
	Yet comes full lately both dinners and drinks,
	But neatly.
	Both our dame and our sire,
	When we have run in the mire,
	They can nip at our hire,
	And pay us full lately.
	But hear my truth, master, for the fare that ye
	make
	I shall do thereafter work, as I take ;
	I shall do a little, sir, and strive and still lack,
	For yet lay my supper never on my stomack
	In fields.
	Whereto should I argue ?
	With my staff can I leap,
	And men say 'a cheap
	Bargain yields badly.'
First Shepherd :	Thou wert an ill lad, to ride on wooing
	With a man that had but little of spending.
Second Shepherd :	Peace, boy !—I bade : no more jangling,
	Or I shall make thee afraid, by the heaven's
	king !
	With thy gawds ;
	Where are our sheep, boy, we scorn ?
Third Shepherd :	Sir, this same day at morn,
	I them left in the corn,
	When they rang lauds ;
	They have pasture good, they cannot go wrong.
First Shepherd :	That is right by the rood, these nights are long,
	Yet I would, or we went, one gave us a song.
Second Shepherd :	So I thought as I stood, to mirth us along.

Third Shepherd:	I grant.
First Shepherd:	Let me sing the tenory.
Second Shepherd:	And I the treble so high.
Third Shepherd:	Then the mean falls to me;
	Let see how ye chaunt.

[*Mac, a sheep-stealer, enters, with a cloak thrown over his smock*]

Mac:	Now, Lord, for thy names seven, that made both moon and stars
	Well more than I can even: thy will, Lord, of my thorns;
	I am all uneven, that moves oft my harness,
	Now would God I were in heaven, for there weep no bairns
	So still.
First Shepherd:	Who is that pipes so poor?
Mac:	Would God ye knew how I fare!
	Lo, a man that walks on the moor,
	And has not all his will.
Second Shepherd:	Mac, where hast thou gone? Tell us tidings.
Third Shepherd:	Is he come? Then each one take heed to his things.

[*Takes his cloak from him*]

Mac:	What, I am a yeoman, I tell you, of the king;
	The self and the same, sent from a great lording,
	And such.
	Fy on you, get thee hence,
	Out of my presence,
	I must have reverence,
	Why, who be I?
First Shepherd:	Why make ye it so quaint? Mac, ye do wrong.
Second Shepherd:	But, Mac, list, ye saint? I trow that ye sang.
Third Shepherd:	I trow the shrew can paint, the devil might him hang!
Mac:	I shall make complaint, and make you all to be flogged.
	At a word,
	And tell even how ye doth.
First Shepherd:	But, Mac, is that sooth?
	Now take out that southern tooth,
	And set in a tord.

Second Shepherd :	Mac, the devil in your eye, a stroke would I lend you.
Third Shepherd :	Mac, know ye not me? By God, I could tell you.
Mac :	God look you all three, methought I had seen you.
	Ye are a fair company.
First Shepherd :	Can ye now moan you?
Second Shepherd :	Shrew, jest!

Thus late as thou goes,
What will men suppose?
And thou hast an ill repute
    Of stealing of sheep.

Mac : And I am true as steel all men wait,
But a sickness I feel, that holds me full hot,
My belly fares not well, it is out of its state.

Third Shepherd : Seldom lies the devil dead by the gate.

Mac :   Therefore
Full sore am I and ill,
If I stand stock still;
I eat not a needle
    This month and more.

First Shepherd : How fares thy wife? By my hood, how fares she?

Mac : Lies weltering! by the rood! by the fire, lo!
And a house full of brats, she drinks well too,
Ill speed other good that she will do;
    But so
Eats as fast as she can,
And each year that comes to man,
She brings forth a plaything,
    And some years two.
But were I not more gracious, and richer by far,
I were eaten out of house, and of harbour,
Yet is she a foul dowse, if ye come near.
There is none that trows, nor knows, a worse
    Than ken I.
Now will ye see what I proffer,
To give all in my coffer
To-morrow next to offer,
    Her head mass-penny.

Second Shepherd:	I wot so forwaked is none in this shire:
	I would sleep if I taked less to my hire.
Third Shepherd:	I am cold and naked, and would have a fire.
First Shepherd:	I am weary from walking, and run in the mire.
	Wake thou!
Second Shepherd:	Nay, I will lie down-by,
	For I must sleep truly.
Third Shepherd:	As good a man's son was I
	As any of you.
	But, Mac, come hither, between us thou shalt lie.
Mac:	Then might I stay you at once: of that ye would say,—
	No dread.
	From my head to my toe
	Manus tuas commendo,
	Pontio Pilato.
	Christ's cross me speed,

                [*He rises, the shepherds still sleeping*]

Now were time for a man, that lacks what he
    wold,
To stalk privately then into a fold
And namely to work then, and be not too bold,
He might abide the bargain, if it were told
    At the ending.
Now were time for to revel;
But he needs good counsel
That fain would fare well,
    And has but little spending.
             [*Mac works a spell on them*]
But about you a circle, as round as a moon,
Till I have done what I will, till that it be
    noon,
That ye lie stone-still, till that I have done,
And I shall say there till of good words a few
    On height;
Over your heads my hand I lift,
Out go your eyes, fore to do your sight,
But yet I must make better shift,
    And it be right.
What, Lord? they sleep hard! that may ye all
    hear;

Was I never a shepherd, but now will I learn
If the flock be scared, yet shall I nap near,
Who draws hitherward, now mends our cheer,
    From sorrow :
A fat sheep I dare say,
A good fleece dare I lay,
Eft white when I may,
    But this will I borrow.

            [*He steals a sheep and goes home*]
                        . . .

Mac: [*at his own door*] : How, Gyll, art thou in?
            Get us some light.

Gyll: Who makes such din this time of night?
            I am set for to spin : I hope not I might
            Rise a penny to win : I shrew them on height.
                So fares
            A housewife that has been
            To be raised thus between :
            There may no note be seen
                For such small jobs.

Mac: Good wife, open the wicket. See'st thou not
            what I bring?

Gyll: I may let thee draw the sneck. Ah! come in,
            my sweeting.

Mac: Yea, thou dost not reck of my long standing.

Gyll: By thy naked neck, thou art like for to hang.

Mac: Go away :
            I am worthy of my meat,
            For in a strait can I get
            More than they that toil and sweat
                All the long day,
            Thus it fell to my lot, Gyll, I had such grace.

Gyll: It were a foul blot to be hanged for the case.

Mac: I have scaped, Jelott, oft as hard as glass.

Gyll: 'But so long goes the pot to the water,' men
            says,
            'At last comes it home broken.'

Mac: Well know I the token,
            But let it never be spoken ;
                But come and help fast.
            I would he were flayn ; I list we'll eat :

	This twelvemonth was I not so fain of one sheep-meat.
Gyll:	Come they if he be slain, and hear the sheep bleat?
Mac:	Then might I be ta'en : that were a cold sweat. Go bar The gate door.
Gyll:	Yes, Mac, For and they come at thy back.
Mac:	Then might I pay for all the pack : The devil of them give warning.
Gyll:	A good jest have I spied, since thou can none : Here shall we him hide, till they be gone; In my cradle abide. Let me alone, And I shall lie beside in childbed and groan.
Mac:	Thou sayest so? And I shall say thou wast light Of a knave child this night.
Gyll:	Now well is my day bright, That ever I was bred. This is a good guise and a far cast : Yet a woman's advice helps at the last. I care never who spies : again go thou fast.
Mac:	But I come or they rise; else blows a cold blast— I will go sleep. [*Mac goes back to the field*] . . .
Mac:	Yet sleep all this company, And I shall go stalk privily, As it had never been I That carried their sheep.
First Shepherd:	*Resurrex à mortrius :* have hold my hand. *Judas carnas dominus,* I may not well stand : My foot sleeps, by Jesus, and I water fastand! I thought that we laid us full near England.
Second Shepherd:	Ah ye! Lord, how I have slept weel! As fresh as an eel, As light I me feel As leaf on a tree.

Third Shepherd:	*Benedicite!* be herein! So my head quakes
	My heart is out of skin, what so it makes.
	Who makes all this din? So my brow aches,
	To the door will I win. Hark fellows, wakes!
	We were four:
	See ye anything of Mac now?
First Shepherd:	We were up ere thou.
Second Shepherd:	Man, I give God a vow,
	Yet heed he nowhere.
Third Shepherd:	Methought he was wrapped in a wolf's-skin.
First Shepherd:	So are many happed, now namely within.
Second Shepherd:	When we had long napped; methought with a gin
	A fat sheep he trapped, but he made no din.
Third Shepherd:	Be still:
	Thy dream makes thee mad:
	It is but phantom, by the rood.
First Shepherd:	Now God turn all to good,
	If it be his will.
Second Shepherd:	Rise, Mac, for shame! thou ly'st right long.
Mac:	Now Christ, his holy name be us among,
	What is this? for Saint James!—I may not well gang,
	I trust I be the same. Ah! my neck has lain wrang
	Enough
	Mickle thank, since yester-even
	Now, by Saint Stephen!
	I was flayed with a dream,—
	My heart out of sloth.
	I thought Gyll began to croak, and travail full sad,
	Well nigh at the first cock,—of a young lad,
	For to mend our flock: then be I never glad.
	To have two on my rock,—more than ever I had.
	Ah, my head!
	A house full of young bellies,
	The devil knock out their brains!
	Woe is he has many bairns,
	And thereto little bread.

	I must go home, by your leave, to Gyll as I thought.
	I pray you look my sleeve, that I steal nought :
	I am loth you to grieve, or from you take aught.
Third Shepherd :	Go forth, ill might thou prosper, now would I we sought,
	This morn,
	That we had all our store.
First Shepherd :	But I will go before,
	Let us meet.
Second Shepherd :	Where?
Third Shepherd :	At the crooked thorn.

· · ·

Mac :	[*at his own door again*] : Undo this door! who is here?
	How long shall I stand?
Gyll :	Who makes such a stir?—Now walk in the waning moon.
Mac :	Ah, Gyll, what cheer?—It is I, Mac, your husband.
Gyll :	Then may we be here,—the devil in a band, Sir Gile.
	Lo, he comes with a lot,
	As he were holden in the throat.
	I may not sit, work or not
	A hand long while.
Mac :	Will ye hear what fare she makes—to get her a lie,
	And do naught but plays—and close her toes.
Gyll :	Why, who wanders, who wakes,—who comes, who goes?
	Who brews, who bakes? Who makes for me this hose?
	And then
	It is ruth to behold,
	Now in hot, now in cold,
	Full woful is the household
	That wants a woman.
	But what end hast thou made with the herds, Mac?

Mac:	The last word that they said,—when I turned my back,
	They would look that they had—their sheep all the pack.
	I hope they will not be well paid,—when they their sheep lack.
	Perdie!
	But howso the game goes,
	To me they will suppose,
	And make a foul noise,
	And cry out upon me.
	But thou must do as thou hight.
Gyll:	I accord me thereto.
	I shall swaddle him right in my cradle.
	If it were a greater slight, yet could I help till.
	I will lie down straight. Come hap me.
Mac:	I will.
Gyll:	Behind,
	Come Coll and his marrow,
	They will nip us full narrow.
Mac:	But I may cry out 'Halloo!'
	The sheep if they find.
Gyll:	Hearken aye when they call: they will come anon.
	Come and make ready all, and sing by thine own,
	Sing 'Lullay!' thou shall, for I must groan,
	And cry out by the wall on Mary and John
	For sore.
	Sing 'Lullay' full fast
	When thou hears at the last;
	And but I play a false cast
	Trust me no more.

[Re-enter the Three Shepherds]

Third Shepherd:	Ah, Coll! good morn:—why sleepest thou not?
First Shepherd:	Alas, that ever was I born!—we have a foul blot.
	A fat wether have we lost.
Third Shepherd:	Marry, God forbid!
Second Shepherd:	Who should do us that scorn? That were a foul spot.

First Shepherd:	Some shrew. I have sought with my dogs, All Horbery Shrubberies[1] And of fifteen hogs Found I but one ewe.
Third Shepherd:	Now trust me if you will;—by Saint Thomas of Kent! Either Mac or Gyll—was at that assent.
First Shepherd:	Peace, man, be still;—I saw when he went. Thou slander'st him ill; thou ought to repent. Good speed.
Second Shepherd:	Now as ever might I thee, If I should even here die, I would say it were he, That did that same deed.
Third Shepherd:	Go we thither I suggest,—and run on our feet. May I never eat bread,—the truth till I wit.
First Shepherd:	Nor drink, in my heed,—with him till I meet.
Second Shepherd:	I will rest in no stead, till that I him greet, My brother One I will call: Till I see him in sight Shall I never sleep one night There I do another.
Third Shepherd:	Will ye hear how they make game,—Our Sire! list, how they croon!
First Shepherd:	Hard I never none crack,—so clear out of tune. Call on him.
Second Shepherd:	Mac! undo your door soon.
Mac:	Who is it that spoke,—as it were noon? On loft, Who is that I say?
Third Shepherd:	Good fellows! were it day?
Mac:	As far as ye may,— Good, speak ye soft! Over a sick woman's head,—that is ill mate ease, I had liefer be dead,—or she had any disease.
Gyll:	Go to another stead; I may not well breathe

[1] Near Wakefield.

	Each foot that ye tread—goes near make me sneeze
	So he!
First Shepherd:	Tell us, Mac, if ye may,
	How fare ye, I say?
Mac:	But are ye in this town to-day?
	Now how fare ye?
	Ye have run in the mire, and are wet yit:
	I shall make you a fire, if ye will sit.
	A horse would I hire; think ye on it.
	Well quit is my hire, my dream—this is it.
	A season.
	I have bairns if ye knew,
	Well more than enough,
	But we must drink as we brew,
	And that is but reason.
	I would ye dined e'er ye went: methink that ye sweat.
Second Shepherd:	Nay, neither mends our mode, drink nor meat.
Mac:	Why, sir, ails you aught, but good?
Third Shepherd:	Yes, our sheep that we gat,
	Are stolen as they grazed. Our loss is great.
Mac:	Sirs, drinkys!
	Had I been there,
	Some should have bought it full dear.
First Shepherd:	Marry, some men trows that ye were,
	And that makes us suspicious.
Second Shepherd:	Mac, some men trows that it should be ye.
Third Shepherd:	Either ye or your spouse; so say we.
Mac:	Now if ye have suspicions to Gyll or to me,
	Come and rip our house, and then may ye see
	Who had her.
	If I any sheep got,
	Either cow or stot,
	And Gyll, my wife rose not
	Here since she laid her.
	As I am both true and leal, to God here I pray,
	That this be the first meal, I shall eat this day.
First Shepherd:	Mac, as I have weal, arise thee, I say!
	'He learned timely to steal, that could not say nay.'

Gyll:	I swelter.
	Out thieves from my once!
	Ye come to rob us for the nonce.
Mac:	Hear ye not how she groans?
	Your heart should melt.
Gyll:	Out thieves, from my bairn! Nigh him not thore.
Mac:	Knew ye how she had farne, your hearts would be sore.
	Ye do wrong, I you warn, that thus commys before
	To a woman that has fared; but I say no more.
Gyll:	Ah, my middle!
	I pray to God so mild,
	If ever I you beguiled,
	That I eat this child,
	That lies in this cradle.
Mac:	Peace, woman, for God's pain, and cry not so:
	Thou spill'st thy brain, and mak'st me full woe.
Second Shepherd:	I know our sheep be slain, what find ye too?
Third Shepherd:	All work we in vain: as well may we go.
	But confound it
	I can find no flesh,
	Hard nor soft
	Salt nor fresh,
	But two bare platters:
	No cattle but this, tame nor wild,
	None, as have I bliss; as loud as he smiled.
Gyll:	No, so God me bliss, and give me joy of my child.
First Shepherd:	We have marked amiss: I hold us beguiled.
Second Shepherd:	Sir, done!
	Sir, our lady him save,
	Is your child a boy?
Mac:	Any lord might him have
	This child to his son.
	When he wakens he skips, that joy is to see.
Third Shepherd:	In good time, be his steps, and happy they be!
	But who was his gossips, tell now to me!

Mac:	So fair fall their lips!
First Shepherd:	[*aside*]: Hark now, a lie!
Mac:	So God them thank,
	Parkin, and Gibbon Waller, I say,
	And gentle John Horne, in good faith,
	He made all the hubbub,
	With the great shank.
Second Shepherd:	Mac, friends will we be, for we are all one.
Mac:	Why! now I hold for me, for help get I none.
	Farewell all three: all glad were ye gone.
Third Shepherd:	Fair words may there be, but love there is none.
First Shepherd:	Gave ye the child anything?
Second Shepherd:	I trust not one farthing.
Third Shepherd:	Fast again will I fling,
	Abide ye me there.
	[*He returns to Mac's cot*]
	Mac, take it to no grief, if I come to thy barn.
Mac:	Nay, thou dost me great reprieve, and foul hast thou done.
Third Shepherd:	The child will it not grieve, that little day-star.
	Mac, with your leave, let me give your bairn, But sixpence.
Mac:	Nay, go 'way: he sleeps.
Third Shepherd:	Methink he peeps.
Mac:	When he wakens he weeps.
	I pray you go hence.
Third Shepherd:	Give me leave him to kiss, and lift up the clout.
	What the devil is this? He has a long snout.
First Shepherd:	He is marked amiss. We wait ill about.
Second Shepherd:	Ill spun weft, I wis, aye cometh foul out;
	Aye so:
	He is like to our sheep.
Third Shepherd:	How, Gib, may I peep?
First Shepherd:	I trow, kind will creep,
	Where it may not go.
Second Shepherd:	This was a false gem, and a far cast
	It was a high fraud.
Third Shepherd:	Yea, sirs, was't.
	Let burn this bawd and bind her fast.
	A false scold hangs at the last;
	So shall thou.

	Will ye see how they swaddle
	His four feet in the middle?
	Saw I never in a cradle
	A horned lad e'er now.

Mac: Peace bid I : what ! let be your fare ;
I am he that him gat, and yond woman him
bare.

First Shepherd: What devil shall be called? Mac, lo, God
makes air.

Second Shepherd: Let be all that. Now God give him care !
I say.

Gyll: A pretty child is he,
As sits upon a woman's knee ;
A dylly-downe, perdie !
To make a man laugh.

Third Shepherd: I know him by the ear mark :—that is a good
token.

Mac: I tell you, sirs, hark :—his nose was broken
Since then, told me a clerk,—that he was be-
witched.

First Shepherd: This is a false work.—I would fain be avenged.
Get a weapon !

Gyll: He was taken for an elf ;
I saw it myself.
When the clock struck twelve,
Was he mis-shapen.

Second Shepherd: Ye two are right deft,—same in a stead.

Third Shepherd: Since they maintain their theft,—let's do them
to dead.

Mac: If I trespass eft, gird off my head.
With you will I be left.

First Shepherd: Sirs, do my red
For this trespass,
We will neither curse nor flout
Fight, nor chide,
But seize him tight,
And cast him in canvas.

[*They toss Mac for his sins*]

. . .

First Shepherd: [*as the three return to the fold*]: Lord, how I
am sore, in point for to tryst :
In faith I may no more, therefore will I rest.

113

H

Second Shepherd:	As a sheep of seven score, he weighed in my fist.
	For to sleep anywhere, methink that I list.
Third Shepherd:	Now I pray you,
	Lie down on this green.
First Shepherd:	On these thefts yet I mean.
Third Shepherd:	Whereto should ye vex about it?
	Do as I say you.
	[Enter an Angel above, who sings 'Gloria in Excelsis']
Angel:	Rise, hired-men, gracious, for now is he born
	That shall take from the fiend, that Adam had lost:
	That warlock to destroy, this night is He born.
	God is made your friend: now at this morn,
	He behests;
	To Bedlem go see,
	There lies that One
	In a crib full poorly,
	Betwixt two beasts.
First Shepherd:	This was a quaint voice that ever yet I heard.
	It is a marvel to relate, thus to be scared.
Second Shepherd:	Of God's son of heaven, he spoke up word.
	All the wood like the lightning, methought that he gard
	Appear.
Third Shepherd:	He spoke of a bairn
	In Bedlem I you warn.
First Shepherd:	That betokens yonder star.
	Let us seek him there.
Second Shepherd:	Say, what was his song? Heard ye not how he cracked it?
	Three breves to a long.
Third Shepherd:	Yea, marry, he shouted it.
	Was no crochet wrong, nor no thing that lacked it.
First Shepherd:	For to sing us among, right as he knacked it, I can.
Second Shepherd:	Let us see how ye croon
	Can ye bark at the moon?
Third Shepherd:	Hold your tongues, have done.

First Shepherd: Hark after, then.
Second Shepherd: To Bedlem he bade—that we should gang :
I am full feared—that we tarry too long.
Third Shepherd: Be merry and not sad : of mirth is our song,
Everlasting glad, our road may we take,
Without noise.
First Shepherd: Hie we thither quickly;
If we be wet and weary,
To that child and that lady
We have it not to dally.
Second Shepherd: We find by the prophecy—let be your din—
Of David and Esai, and more than I can
mind ;
They prophesied by clergy, that on a virgin
Should he light and ly, to pardon our sin
And slake it,
Our kind from woe ;
For Esai said so,
Cite virgo
Concipiet a child that is naked.
Third Shepherd: Full glad may we be,—and abide that day
That lovely to see,—that all mights may.
Lord, well for me,—for once and for aye,
Might I kneel on my knee—some word for to
say
To that child.
But the angel said
In a crib was he laid ;
He was poorly arrayed,
Both meaner and mild.
First Shepherd: Patriarchs that have been,—and prophets be-
forn,
They desired to have seen—this child that is
born.
They are gone full clean—that have they lorn.
We shall see him, I ween,—e'er it be morn
By token
When I see him and feel,
Then know I full weel
It is true as steel
That prophets have spoken.

115

To so poor that we are, that he would appear,
First find, and declare by his messenger.

Second Shepherd: Go we now, let us fare: the place is us near.

Third Shepherd: I am ready and eager, go we in fear
    To that light!
Lord! if thy wills be,
We are unlearn'd all three,
Thou grant us of thy grace,
    To comfort thy wight.

       •   •   •

          [*The Shepherds arrive at Bethlehem*]

First Shepherd: Hail, comely and clean; hail, young child!
Hail, maker, as I mean, of a maiden so mild!
Thou hast wared, I ween, off the evil one so
    wild,
The false guiler of teen, now goes He beguiled.
    Lo, He merry is!
Lo, He laughs, my sweeting,
A welcome meeting!
I have given my greeting
    Have a bob of cherries.

Second Shepherd: Hail, sovereign saviour, for thou hast us
    sought!
Hail freely, leaf and flow'r, that all thing has
    wrought!
Hail full of flavour, that made all of nought!
Hail! I kneel and I cower. A bird have I
    brought
    To my bairn!
Hail, little tiny-pate,
Of our creed thou art crop!
I would drink in thy cup,
    Little day-star.

Third Shepherd: Hail, darling dear, full of godheed!
I pray thee be near, when that I have need.
Hail! sweet is thy cheer: my heart would
    bleed
To see thee sit here in so poor weed
    With no pennies.
Hail! put forth thy hand!—

116

I bring thee but a ball
Have and play thee with all,
  And go to the tennis.

Mary: The Father of Heaven, God omnipotent,
That set all alight, his son has he sent.
My name could he tell, and laugh as he
    weened.
I conceived him full even, through might, as
    God meant;
  And new is he born.
He keep you from woe:
I shall pray him so;
Tell forth as ye go,
  And mind on this morn.

First Shepherd: Farewell lady, so fair to behold,
With thy child on thy knee.

Second Shepherd: But he lies full cold,
Lord, well is me: now we go forth, behold!

Third Shepherd: Forsooth, already it seems to be told
  Full oft.

First Shepherd: What grace we have found.

Second Shepherd: Come forth, now are we won.

Third Shepherd: To sing are we bound:
Let us sing it aloft.

ANONYMOUS (Thirteenth–Fifteenth Centuries)

MIDNIGHT

The houre when Spirits walke, and Cats goe
a-gossipping.

THOMAS DEKKER, 1570–1641

NOEL

God save you all, this Christmas night,
let nothing you dismay;
for, say, if He'd preferred the light
of Heaven to lantern-ray,
the sanctus of His seraph-choir
to shepherd pipe and donkey bray,
would you and I be on our way
home from His Mass to meat and fire?

SANDYS WASON, 1867–1950

THE FRANKELEYN'S 'NOWEL'

Upon the morwe, whan that it was day,
To Britaigne tooké they the righté way,—
Aurelius and this magicien bisyde,
And been descended ther they wolde abyde;
And this was, as thise bookés me remembre,
The coldé, frosty sesoun of Decembre.

Phebus wox old, and hewéd lyk latoun,
That in his hooté declynacioun
Shoon as the burnéd gold, with stremés brighte;
But now in Capricorn adoun he lighte,
Where as he shoon ful pale, I dar wel seyn.
The bittré frostes with the sleet and reyn
Destroyéd hath the grene in every yerd:
Janus sit by the fyr with double berd,
And drynketh of his bugle horn the wyn;
Biforn hym stant brawn of the tuskéd swyn,
And 'Nowel' crieth every lusty man.

GEOFFREY CHAUCER, 1340–1400

'HE COUDN'T SPEL'

S O M E kind person has sent me Chawcer's poems. Mr C. had
talent, but he coudn't spel. No man has a right to be a lit'rary
man onless he knows how to spel. It is a pity that Chawcer, who
had geneyus, was so unedicated. He's the wus speller I know of.

ARTEMUS WARD, 1834–67

ARCHBISHOP BECKET'S SERMON, 1170

' G L O R Y to God in the highest, and on earth peace to men of
good will.' The fourteenth verse of the second chapter of the
Gospel according to Saint Luke. In the Name of the Father, and
of the Son, and of the Holy Ghost. Amen.

Dear children of God, my sermon this Christmas morning will
be a very short one. I wish only that you should meditate in
your hearts the deep meaning and mystery of our masses of
Christmas Day. For whenever Mass is said, we re-enact the
Passion and Death of Our Lord; and on this Christmas Day we
do this in celebration of His Birth. So that at the same moment
we rejoice in His coming for the salvation of men, and offer
again to God His Body and Blood in sacrifice, oblation and
satisfaction for the sins of the whole world. It was in this same
night that has just passed, that a multitude of the heavenly host
appeared before the shepherds at Bethlehem, saying 'Glory to
God in the highest, and on earth peace to men of good will';
at this same time of all the year that we celebrate at once the
Birth of Our Lord and His Passion and Death upon the Cross.
Beloved, as the World sees, this is to behave in a strange fashion.
For who in the World will both mourn and rejoice at once and
for the same reason? For either joy will be overborne by mourning, or mourning will be cast out by joy; so it is only in these our
Christian mysteries that we can rejoice and mourn at once for
the same reason. Now think for a moment about the meaning of
this word 'peace.' Does it seem strange to you that the angels
should have announced Peace, when ceaselessly the world has
been stricken with War and the fear of War? Does it seem to
you that the angelic voices were mistaken, and that the promise
was a disappointment and a cheat?

Reflect now, how Our Lord Himself spoke of Peace. He said

to His disciples, 'My peace I leave with you, my peace I give unto you.' Did He mean peace as we think of it: the kingdom of England at peace with its neighbours, the barons at peace with the King, the householder counting over his peaceful gains, the swept hearth, his best wine for a friend at the table, his wife singing to the children? Those men His disciples knew no such things: they went forth to journey afar, to suffer by land and sea, to know torture, imprisonment, disappointment, to suffer death by martyrdom. What then did He mean? If you ask that, remember then that He said also, 'Not as the world gives, give I unto you.' So then, He gave to His disciples peace, but not peace as the world gives.

Consider also one thing of which you have probably never thought. Not only do we at the feast of Christmas celebrate at once Our Lord's Birth and His Death: but on the next day we celebrate the martyrdom of His first martyr, the blessed Stephen. Is it an accident, do you think, that the day of the first martyr follows immediately the day of the Birth of Christ? By no means. Just as we rejoice and mourn at once, in the Birth and in the Passion of Our Lord; so, also, in a smaller figure, we both rejoice and mourn in the death of martyrs. We mourn, for the sins of the world that has martyred them; we rejoice, that another soul is numbered among the Saints in Heaven, for the glory of God and for the salvation of men.

Beloved, we do not think of a martyr simply as a good Christian who has been killed because he is a Christian: for that would be solely to mourn. We do not think of him simply as a good Christian who has been elevated to the company of the Saints: for that would be simply to rejoice: and neither our mourning nor our rejoicing is as the world's is. A Christian martyrdom is never an accident, for Saints are not made by accident. Still less is a Christian martyrdom the effect of a man's will to become a Saint, as a man by willing and contriving may become a ruler of men. A martyrdom is always the design of God, for His love of men, to warn them and to lead them, to bring them back to His ways. It is never the design of man; for the true martyr is he who has become the instrument of God, who has lost his will in the will of God, and who no longer desires anything for himself, not even the glory of being a martyr. So thus as on earth, the Church mourns and rejoices at once, in a fashion that the world cannot understand; so in

Heaven the Saints are most high, having made themselves most low, and are seen, not as we see them, but in the light of the Godhead from which they draw their being.

I have spoken to you to-day, dear children of God, of the martyrs of the past, asking you to remember especially our martyr of Canterbury, the blessed Archbishop Elphege; because it is fitting, on Christ's birth day, to remember what is that Peace which He brought; and because, dear children, I do not think I shall ever preach to you again; and because it is possible that in a short time you may have yet another martyr, and that one perhaps not the last. I would have you keep in your hearts these words that I say, and think of them at another time. In the Name of the Father, and of the Son, and of the Holy Ghost. Amen.

T. S. ELIOT, 1888–

THE CRADLE OF TRUE LOVE

A N D go to Mary and make covenant with her, to keep her child, not for her need but for thine. And take to thee the sweet child and sweetly swathe it in his cradle with sweet love bands. Put from thee the cradle of self love and draw to thee the cradle of true love, for that liketh this child to rest him in, and so in thy soul sing lovelike and say:

> Lovely little child, fairest of hue,
> Have mercy on me, sweet Jesu.

And the while thou thus singest, be sorry and think how oft thou hast received thy God and laid him in a foul common stable to all the seven deadly sins . . . and seldom fully cleansed to God's liking; therefore oft sigh and sorrow and shrive thee to God as thou rockest the cradle, and sing and say: *Lovely little Child*.

ANONYMOUS (FIFTEENTH CENTURY)

SON OF THE HOUSE

> Maiden of night, the star
> Steadies for you. Hold up
> Now your purposed cup
> For the straight fall of fire.

The archangels like storks to earth
Drop where you bow and bring forth,
More eloquent than prophets and law
The rustle in your house of straw,

And to men naked of sinning
The breath of a stable is kind.
No lack, no fault, no end,
In such fullness, perfection, beginning.

But she who holds her cup for a jewel of fire to fill
Watches the water and blood rise   brim   spill
Until the spate of the appalling river sweeps between night and
    day
And none to comfort the giver none to staunch to allay
Save a golden child rustling
Live as a merry mouse
The innocent heart's nestling
The son of a straw house.   FRANCES BELLERBY

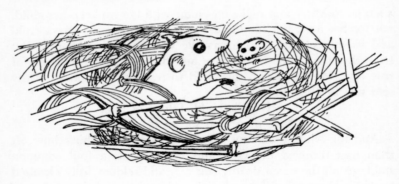

JEWISH PROVERB

G O D could not be everywhere and therefore he made mothers.

UNKNOWN

BY WAY OF A PREFACE . . .

N A T I V I T Y poems are of every century and decade; their poets
do not borrow, but re-interpret.

GEORGE Y. JUSTIN, 1909–

ON THE NATIVITIE

Rorate coeli desuper!
   Hevins, distil your balmy schouris!
For now is risen the bricht day-ster
   Fro the rose Mary, flour of flouris:
   The cleir Sone, quhom no cloud devouris,
Surmounting Phebus in the Est,
   Is cumin of his hevinly touris:
   Et nobis Puer natus est.

Archangellis, angellis, and dompnationis,
   Tronis, potestatis, and marteiris seir,
And all ye hevinly operationis,
   Ster, planeit, firmament, and spheir,
   Fire, erd, air, and water cleir,
To Him gife loving, most and lest,
   That come in to so meik maneir;
   Et nobis Puer natus est.

Synnaris be glad, and penance do,
   And thank your Maker hairtfully;
For He that ye micht nocht come to
   To you is cumin full humbly
   Your soulis with his blood to buy
And loose you of the fiendis arrest—
   And only of his ain mercy;
   Pro nobis Puer natus est.

All clergy do to him inclyne,
   And bow unto that Bairn benyng,
And do your observance divyne
   To him that is of kingis King:
   Encense his altar, read and sing
In holy kirk, with mind degest,
   Him honouring attour all thing
   Qui nobis Puer natus est.

Celestial foulis in the air,
   Sing with your nottis upon hicht,
In firthis and in forrestis fair
   Be myrthful now at all your mycht;

For passit is your dully night,
Aurora has the cloudis perst,
    The Sone is risen with glaidsum licht,
    Et nobis Puer natus est.

Now spring up flouris fra the rute,
    Revert you upward naturaly,
In honour of the blissit frute
    That raiss up fro the rose Mary;
    Lay out your levis lustily,
Fro deid take life now at the lest
    In wirschip of that Prince worthy
    Qui nobis Puer natus est.

Sing, hevin imperial, most of hicht!
    Regions of air mak armony!
All fish in flud and fowl of flicht
    Be mirthful and mak melody!
    All *Gloria in excelsis* cry!
Heaven, erd, se, man, bird, and best—
    He that is crownit abone the sky
    Pro nobis Puer natus est!

WILLIAM DUNBAR, 1465–1520

A HYMN
ON THE NATIVITIE OF MY SAVIOUR

I sing the birth, was born tonight,
The Author both of Life, and light;
    The Angels so did sound it,
And like the ravish'd Sheep'erds said,
Who saw the light, and were afraid,
    Yet search'd, and true they found it.

The Sonne of God, th' Eternall King,
That did us all salvation bring,
    And freed the soule from danger;
Hee whom the whole world could not take,
The Word, which heaven, and earth did make;
    Was now laid in a Manger.

The Father's wisedome will'd it so,
The Sonne's obedience knew no No,
      Both wills were in one stature;
And as that wisedome had decreed,
The Word was now made Flesh indeed,
      And tooke on him our Nature.

What comfort by him do wee winne?
Who made himselfe the price of sinne,
      To make us heires of glory?
To see this Babe, all innocence;
A Martyr born in our defence;
      Can man forget this Storie?

BEN JONSON, 1573-1637

THE NATIVITY OF OUR LORD

Where is this stupendous stranger,
   Swains of Solyma, advise,
Lead me to my Master's manger,
   Shew me where my Saviour lies?

O Most Mighty! O MOST HOLY!
   Far beyond the seraph's thought,
Art thou then so mean and lowly
   As unheeded prophets taught?

O the magnitude of meekness!
   Worth from worth immortal sprung;
O the strength of infant weakness,
   If eternal is so young!

If so young and thus eternal,
   Michael tune the shepherd's reed,
Where the scenes are ever vernal,
   And the loves be love indeed!

See the God blasphemed and doubted
   In the schools of Greece and Rome;
See the pow'rs of darkness routed,
   Taken at their utmost gloom.

Nature's decorations glisten
    Far above their usual trim;
Birds on box and laurel listen,
    As so near the cherubs hymn.

Boreas now no longer winters
    On the desolated coast;
Oaks no more are riv'n in splinters
    By the whirlwind and his host.

Spinks and ouzels sing sublimely,
    'We too have a Saviour born';
Whiter blossoms burst untimely
    On the blest Mosaic thorn.

God all-bounteous, all-creative,
    Whom no ills from good dissuade.
Is incarnate, and a native
    Of the very world he made.

CHRISTOPHER SMART, 1722-71

NATIVITY

All creatures then rejoiced, save that the Seven
    Capital steers of whom I am a herder
        (My cloven heart their hoofprint in the mire)
With bloodshot glare interrogated heaven,
    And, back to back, with lowered horns of murder
        From spiracles of fury spirted fire.

Never so joyfully the brave cocks crew—
    No more by turns, but all with one accord.
        Never so early woke the mule and ox
Since it was day before the east was blue:
    Mary the dawn, the Sunrise was the Lord,
        And Joseph was the watchtower on the rocks.

Never for such a golden quilt lay blooming
    The fields, as for this richly-laden hay,
        And though the frost was fierce before the day,
The mule and ox, whose respiration fuming
    Ignited in the lantern's dim, red ray,
        Warmed Him with rosy feathers where He lay.

Far overhead streamed on the signal meteor,
    The Ariadne of the maps, who slowly
        Unwound the light and reeled the darkness up.
Love filled with fierce delight the humblest creature
    As heaven fills an eye, or as the Holy
        Infinitude the wafer and the cup.

Shepherds and kings and cowboys knelt around
    And marvelled that, while they could feel the power
        Whose rapture roars in God, yet God should moan :
And while His glory raised men off the ground
    (For Eve had brought such jewels in her dower)
        The tears of man should shine in God alone.

ROY CAMPBELL, 1902–56

THE SWAN

IT was on the third day I saw the swan. It hadn't been at all easy to see. The sky seemed to touch me, to entomb me. The gloom of the blizzard and the industrial pall merged into a funereal umbrella and the wind blinded me, screaming over the flat wastes and whipping a mixture of snow and sawdust into my eyes. But on the afternoon of the third day the pall lifted, and I screwed up my bloodshot eyes, staring out over the ice. Yes, it was a swan, a hundred yards or so away—over towards the centre of the large pool.

It was the worst winter in living memory. Throughout November the weather had been unvarying. No fog or rain, little wind, but cold. Unusually, achingly cold. Early in December the snow came. 'Ah !' said the optimists, 'it will be warmer now,' but this wasn't to be the usual winter—unpleasant but not too extreme. The main roads were cleared (after a fashion) but elsewhere the snow remained, frozen solid. Instead of the expected thaw, the temperature dropped lower. Over everything was a white cap of death. Birds died and gulls swarmed in from the distant sea, beating hopelessly over the frozen canals.

It was the second winter after the Hitler war, and the chronic shortage of coal became acute. The transport system was in chaos and pitheads couldn't be cleared : many factories closed down. Christmas was near, but the majority of unemployed had savings. For me it had been a lean year, and my job—precarious at the best of times—now seemed hopeless. The pool, in fact, often my last resource, was now my only hope. For the waste places were more than ever waste : the ravaged ground—mountains and mazes of slag, grotesque convolutions—on which refuse was dumped was now inaccessible or dangerously hazardous : like a convulsed icecap.

But the lane leading to the pool was flat, without ditches or hedgerows and the pool wasn't a lawn's length from it. There were *two* pools really, but it hardly seemed so ; they were within feet of each other, one large, quite a lake ; by comparison the other was a duckpond. But the small pool (shallow, a stranger would have thought) was deep, very deep, and remote somehow —the secret sort of place that I had always liked. Near enough to the forges, the foundry filth, but *beyond* it : a mile or so and the fields rose westerly towards Shropshire and the sea.

The regular tips were far off, nearer the heart of the Black Country, but—even in summer—there were blank days or weeks when they would yield nothing, and I always turned then towards the pool. Not that I made much. It was supposed to be 'private,' but some drivers would drop their loads anywhere sooner than pay the small toll demanded by the tip bosses. Most loads, of course, shot down into the water, and that was that, but some drivers were so nervous that they dumped their stuff on the bank and roared away with their tailboards flapping.

With Christmas near, the pool was my only hope. Few factories were working, but there would be a general clean-up. Many drivers might think of the pool.

I was disappointed. There was nothing new, only three icy mounds—three loads that seemed to have been there for weeks. I was disappointed but not disheartened—indeed, I was most thankful, relieved to find *something*, and set to work with a will, smashing away the ice with a clump hammer and small pick. Bits of ice fizzed at my face, and my swollen ungloved hands took on a bluey colour—as though ink had been poured over them.

From the first I had a feeling that a living creature was near me, but I wasn't sure. And when—on the third day—I saw the swan I was concerned but not amazed. There were (in summer) usually two or three pairs of swans on the large pool. Swans in dozens favour our filthy Black Country canals, but they often cannot be persuaded to grace lakes set in lovely surroundings. No, I wasn't surprised to see the swan, but its situation surprised me. It was—a shrouded frigate on a frozen sea—trapped, imprisoned, set immovably in the ice.

The next morning I took a bag of bread and walked gingerly out over the ice. I was more than a bit afraid. The ice should be safe, up to a foot thick, but here and there it had a sinister blackish tinge. Several times I was helpless before the wind, and it was then—when I stood helplessly—that the ice seemed to give a little. Some of the stuff dumped into the pool was chemical, and floated on or near the surface. It was, I thought, possible that it might work on the ice. I retreated to the bank, weighed the bag with a lump of slag, and walked out again over the frozen pool. When I was near enough I hurled the bag. Although it fell within inches the swan did not—so far as I could see—so much as blink.

As the days passed I changed my tactics. There was no improvement in the weather, and my own situation was unenviable. During that first hour or so—smashing the ice from the mounds of slag and sawdust-like plating factory-rubbish—I had been warm, but afterwards I was so cold that I nearly wept. Every day I bent low over the waste, sifting it again and again for tiny bits of copper and brass. For hours I would be in the same posture, and my circulation—never good—seemed to cease altogether. All of me seemed dead. I could feel nothing, think nothing: in alarm I would look around me at the white wilderness, but there was no reassurance; I scarcely knew who I was or what I was.

But from the fifth day I glanced often towards the swan—it was *there,* even when I couldn't see it. Every hour or so I took a few scraps of bread and walked out over the frozen pool to feed it. It seemed not a bit grateful—quite the opposite. It was aloof, majestically indifferent, eyeing me disdainfully and hissing quite audibly. As the days passed I noticed a rim of water around the swan, as though the heat of its body was melting the ice. This made me happy, and I ran exultantly up and down when I was back on land.

I

But financially, the outlook was as unrelenting as the weather. Not one load came to the pool. Every day I sifted—again and again—through the old rubbish, and every day I made a few shillings: ominously few. And then, around noon on Christmas Eve, came a load that was full of stuff. I had given up hope of anything like a festive Christmas, and now I worked frenziedly: in three or four hours time the scrap dealers would be closing their yards for the holiday.

I wasn't cold now. The temperature was way below freezing, but I sweated freely. At last—scarcely able to believe my good fortune—I stood back, then something made me turn sharply. It was the swan, flapping its wings and advancing on me.

Wild swans can be surprisingly vicious. For a moment I was uncertain, but the swan waddled up to me, nuzzling my hand like a dog. With the snow falling gently we stared at each other. 'Happy Christmas, Mr. Swan,' I said. 'Better than we expected, eh?'

JOHN PETTY, 1919–

A THAMES DOLPHIN

A.D. 1392: King Richard with Queene Anne his wife, foure bishops, as many Earles, the Duke of Yorke, many Lords, and fifteene Ladies held a royall Christmas at Langley neere to St. Albans. The same Christmas Day a Dolphin came foorth of the Sea and played himselfe in ye Thames at London to the bridge, foreshewing happily the tempests that were to follow within a week after, the which Dolphin being seene of the Citizens, and followed, was with much difficulty intercepted, and brought againe to London, shewing a spectacle to many, of the height of his body, for hee was ten foote in length. These Dolphins are fishes of the Sea that follow the voices of men, and rejoice in the playing of instruments and are wont to gather themselves at musicke. These when they play in rivers, with

hasty springings or leapings doe signifie Tempest to follow. The
Seas containe nothing more swift nor nimble, for sometimes with
their skips, they mount over the sailes of ships.

JOHN STOW, 1525–1605

A LONDON CELEBRATION, 1762

Saturday 25 December: The night before I did not rest well. I
was really violently in love with Louisa. I thought she did not
care for me. I thought that if I did not gain her affections, I
would appear despicable to myself. This day I was in a better
frame, being Christmas day, which has always inspired me with
most agreeable feelings. I went to St. Paul's Church and in that
magnificent temple fervently adored the God of goodness and
mercy, and heard a sermon by the Bishop of Oxford on the
publishing of glad tidings of great joy. I then went to Child's,
where little was passing. However, here goes the form of a

Dialogue at Child's

1 Citizen. Why, here is the bill of mortality. Is it right,
Doctor?

Physician. Why, I don't know.

1 Citizen. I'm sure it is not. Sixteen only died of cholics! I
dare say you have killed as many yourself.

2 Citizen. Ay, and hanged but three! O Lord, ha! ha! ha!

I then sat a while at Coutts's, and then at Macfarlane's, and then went to Davies's. Johnson was gone to Oxford. I was introduced to Mr. Dodsley, a good, jolly, decent, conversable man, and Mr. Goldsmith, a curious, odd, pedantic fellow with some genius. It was quite a literary dinner. I had seen no warm victuals for four days, and therefore played a very bold knife and fork. It is inconceivable how hearty I eat and how comfortable I felt myself after it. We talked entirely in the way of Geniuses.

We talked of poetry. Said Goldsmith, 'The miscellaneous poetry of this age is nothing like that of the last; it is very poor. Why there, now, Mr. Dodsley, is your *Collection.*' Dodsley. 'I think that equal to those made by Dryden and Pope.' Goldsmith. 'To consider them, Sir, as villages, yours may be as good; but let us compare house with house, you can produce me no edifices equal to the *Ode on St. Cecilia's Day, Absalom and Achitophel,* or *The Rape of the Lock.*' Dodsley. 'We have poems in a different way. There is nothing of the kind in the last age superior to *The Spleen.*' Boswell. 'And what do you think of Gray's odes? Are not they noble?' Goldsmith. 'Ah, the rumbling thunder! I remember a friend of mine was very fond of Gray. "Yes," said I, "he is very fine indeed; as thus—

> Mark the white and mark the red,
> Mark the blue and mark the green;
> Mark the colours ere they fade,
> Darting thro' the welkin sheen."

"O, yes," said he, "great, great!" "True, Sir," said I, "but I have made the lines this moment."' Boswell. 'Well, I admire Gray prodigiously. I have read his odes till I was almost mad.' Goldsmith. 'They are terribly obscure. We must be historians and learned men before we can understand them.' Davies. 'And why not? He is not writing to porters or carmen. He is writing to men of knowledge.' Goldsmith. 'Have you seen *Love in a Village?*' Boswell. 'I have. I think it a good, pleasing thing.' Goldsmith. 'I am afraid we will have no good plays now. The taste of the audience is spoiled by the pantomime of Shakespeare. The wonderful changes and shiftings.' Davies. 'Nay, but you will allow that Shakespeare has great merit?' Goldsmith. 'No, I know Shakespeare very well.' (Here I said nothing, but thought him a most impudent puppy.) Boswell. 'What do you think of John-son?' Goldsmith. 'He has exceeding great merit. His *Rambler* is a noble work.' Boswell. 'His *Idler* too is very pretty. It is a lighter performance; and he has thrown off the classical fetters very much.' Davies. 'He is a most entertaining companion. And how can it be otherwise, when he has so much imagination, has read so much, and digested it so well?'

We had many more topics which I don't remember. I was very well. I then went to Macfarlane's. We were very merry. Erskine and I had some bread and wine and talked for near two hours. He told me that he was kept as a blackguard when he was a boy, then went to sea, and then came into the Army. And that he wondered how he had been turned out a tolerable being.

JAMES BOSWELL, 1740–95

BUCHAREST, *1888*

WHAT an amusing morning you must be having—I wonder what you have got for Christmas presents. I came down to breakfast this morning with my arms full of all the presents from Sloane Street which were opened in the dining room. It's not at all a nice Christmas day here, for it is damp and rainy and the streets are inches deep in mud, in fact it is almost impossible to walk. All the poor women here wear short skirts and long top boots so that they don't get muddy at all. They don't wear hats but they tie little coloured shawls all round their heads. You should see the coachmen, they are splendid! They wear long black velvet clothes exactly like a woman's dress, round their waist they tie scarlet woollen scarves and on their heads they have fur caps. The Roumanian language is so like French that one can understand all the words written up on the shops. This evening Auntie Mary is going to have a Christmas dinner party with a real English plum pudding. . . .

Footnote by her sister: The real English plum-pudding was not a great success. For the 'excellent cook,' told by his mistress to boil it, did not understand that it had to be boiled in its cloth. He put it, loose, into a saucepan of water, and to the horror of the company, a greasy soup with floating bits of candied peel, currants and so on, was presently served up. . . .

GERTRUDE BELL, 1868–1926

133

I N those days my life was as circumscribed as that of early man. My territory was limited to four or five Paddington streets, and to a seemingly endless avenue, bordered with gigantic stucco colonnades, which led me to the Park. The frontier was marked by a lion, a red lion with its tail stuck out stiffly behind it; it lived on the roof of a public house, and roared all day long, silently, at the passing trains in the cutting beneath it.

The frontier was not only a frontier; it was the horizon. To pass beyond it was, for me, to become disorientated. When I did so, I felt like a space traveller. Twice a year a four-wheeler loomed up out of the unknown, and my parents and I seated ourselves in it, our feet rustling in the straw. It carried us slowly away. It was an event as inevitable as the procession of the equinoxes. Only once did it fail to occur, and on that day too, the red lion was no longer to be seen. My parents and I crept along the pavement outside our house, striking matches; a dense fog muffled all sound except the shrill chirring of cab whistles. Dimly I saw a patch of frost-whitened straw in the road, and was told that someone must be very ill, nearby. A black day. There was no miracle, and I went back disconsolately to the house. But then a subsidiary miracle did occur. My father broke the seals of one of the parcels which normally were kept inviolate until the Day itself . . . I felt somewhat shocked . . . it was like David trifling with the shewbread . . . there were ninepins inside it, and I forgot my chagrin.

Normally, however, I could rely on being wafted through mysterious London. There were huge, nameless buildings, vast tracts of green prairie which I took to be unexplored parks, unfamiliar green omnibuses spouting steam at every orifice and dropping live coals on the cobbled roadway. . . .

There was only one object I could be certain of recognising amongst all these phantasmagoria, the London Brighton and South Coast station, the home of the Ellbooscroor (L.B.S.C.R.) trains, as I used to call them. No doubt the first outer space traveller will feel as reassured as I did then, knowing that in spite of all the weirdness round him, he will in the end land on the homely object with which he has been familiar since he first opened his eyes.

I admired the engines in the dark cavern. They all wore haloes of bright golden brass round their funnels, their sides were slabs of a pleasing chocolate colour, and their cabs were as delicately tapered as the hips of a Gibson girl. One of them carried our train out into the wintry sunshine. More unexplored and unexplainable territory came into view. My parents were sleepy and were not disposed to answer the thousand and one questions I found it essential to ask in order to locate points of geography. I would have been none the wiser if they had done so . . . what is the good of asking how far off Pernambuco is, if you are unaware that there is a country called Brazil?

The country. . . . I knew that this great entity lay somewhere far away, beyond the chimney tops, and that we were stealthily approaching it. There were several false alarms, in the shape of allotments and playing fields, municipal parks, and large estates, and my frequent wild shouts of acclamation began finally to grate on my parents' ears. When it did appear, at last, I became silent. There were crows stalking about the ragged looking fields, nodding evilly to one another. There were patches of dirty snow on the grass, looking like gobbets of my pet aversion, rice pudding. The sun looked like a huge crimson gong, and it was masked by the intertwinings of black, skeletal branches. Hills began to glide past the carriage windows, low hills which gradually became larger and larger, until they seemed to me to be mountains. I asked whether they were mountains, hoping to find out that we were then crossing America. . . . But we were only in Surrey, climbing up the North Downs. In those days I imagined that the Isle of Wight was covered in eternal ice.

It was a sad grey afternoon, and twilight fell long before the journey was over. Darkness came. There were many stops, with a groaning of wheels and a hissing of brakes. Somebody with a lantern called out 'Rowfant! Rowfant!' There was a rustling of wind, a scrunching of feet in gravel, a distant panting coming from the engine, and there was a drowsy murmur of voices in the next compartment. Then I fell asleep.

When I awoke, I was being carried towards the brougham, which was waiting for us under a street lamp, in Forest Row. My grandmother was dimly to be seen, sitting inside it. There was a glimpse of a lace cap, with a blue ribbon twining through it, and a glitter of jet beads.

Soon we plunged into the outskirts of Ashdown Forest. The sparse lights of Forest Row had disappeared, friendly, fleeting glances. . . . Only the carriage lamps remained, lighting up the undergrowth and the great tree trunks in pools of faded gold. They were handsome, these lamps, with their black cowls and the long white metal stalks which fitted delicately into their sockets, like flower stalks into vases. Their flames were nourished by stout columns of yellow wax. They looked edible, and I began to understand why Russians ate them. How I would have liked to have had one at my bedside, instead of the ordinary anæmic candles which were far too feeble to repel the monsters of the night. I felt safe, even whilst passing through these macabre woods. The tree trunks scowled, and their hide was glairy and pock-marked; the undergrowth writhed and clutched at the sides of the carriage with furry or thorny tentacles which were of a deathly green-grey hue. Icy rain dripped from the few surviving leaves, beating a malicious tattoo on the roof. An owl fluttered down suddenly, an explosion of buff feathers, and swivelled its inky black orbs round to outstare me, with chilly menace.

I listened distractedly to the conversation of my elders. It was a hollow, mysterious sound, and their voices were hushed, as if they too were overawed by the woods. I could make but little of what they were saying; in those days I had the impression that the bizarre language they talked was employed by them only when children were present, and that when they were by themselves they became colloquial, natural, and real people. Then I caught a few words. My grandmother was saying that the postmistress had a bad heart, and was lying in bed. Hearts. . . . I had seen them in the butchers, and one day my mother had bought a pound of heart, and I had eaten some of it. There was also the story of the hero who had slain the dragon and had licked his fingers after plucking out its heart, thus acquiring the faculty of understanding what the birds were saying.

The voices became more and more remote. . . . I saw the postmistress lying in bed, with a large red object protruding through her red flannel nightdress . . . she fumed a little through the green reptilian beak which rested on her lace pillow. A very disturbing dream. I woke up with a start and a cry. We were then getting near Wych Cross. Peter the horse was still walking. I could have wished that his hooves had not echoed so loudly in the silence of the night. The house at the crossroads was as black as ink, with no sign of life in it . . . but at any moment a furious old bell dam might have rushed out of it, menacing us all with her broom.

We got past it in safety, and then we were on the moonlit heath. The heather sparkled like grey, frosted hair. Peter broke into a trot. Something had once happened to his throat, and in it he wore an elaborate apparatus of white metal which looked like a safety valve. It was always blowing copious bubbles. As he trotted he whooped like a Red Indian. It seemed to me that the sound was frightening enough to chase away any bad influence. The post office came into sight; in the summer it was a reassuring place, with yellow bells of beehives round it which perfumed the air with honey, but now I felt uncomfortable. I looked away from it until we were well past it.

That night I found a large baked apple by my bedside. I thought suddenly of the postmistress's heart, and was unable to touch it.

The next day was a day of preparation, and of mounting excitement for me. The family had been assembled; all the aunts and uncles and cousins were there, except for one wicked uncle who had married a barmaid, after running away to fight in the Boer War. A double crime, which had not yet been forgiven. They were not up when I rose. I went out and found a cheese dish on the lawn. I lifted its lid, and smelt the gorgonzola within with great relish. My grandfather's tastes in cheese were frowned on in the family, and his tit-bits were banished from the house. I heard him tinkling away presently on a clavichord he had made himself out of a dressing-table. I went to a window and found him at it. He wore side whiskers and a tam o' shanter. He lifted me up with hands that trembled, and I was glad when I was set down again.

Guests came from the neighbouring houses, rolling up in victorias, landaus, broughams, and other vehicles. The coachmen alighted from their boxes, dressed in green livery, with tall black cockaded silk hats, and brown top boots. They made their way to the kitchen, murmuring obscurely in Sussex dialect. The cook, who was also Sussex, used to reproduce it for me in such sentences as 'Cain't you leave dem dere little rahbuts alone, dere den?'

At lunch that day the great treat was to have been a large piece of beef which my grandmother had salted down herself some long time before . . . but when the time came, the beef did not appear. The cook, thinking that it was a plebeian dish, had imagined that the quality could not possibly eat it, and had fed it to the coachmen.

Those were the last days of the coachmen, and of the carriages, with their spindly, gaily painted wheels. Already there were one or two motor cars abroad, covering the hedges in summer with thick white dust, ploughing up the roads in winter, and disturbing the peaceful sleep of the drunks as they lay, half-way in, halfway out of the ditches. Those were almost the last days, too, of charity soup, of the watery liquid made out of bones and turnips, which my grandmother doled out to the needy villagers.

My grandfather was a retired lead pipe manufacturer, and felt that he was very much the squire in the village; but at that time the influence of the squire was waning. My aunt, his only daughter, used to complain that the villagers no longer touched their caps to her as she passed. The Christmas feast itself, with its Yule log christenings, and its invocation of 'A Merry Christmas and a Happy New Year, and Pray God Bless us and Speed,' its ritual spiced ale, and so on, was very much the same as those embarked upon by all the other would be squires in the neighbourhood. They too entertained their numerous families, summoned from far and wide. The aunts, uncles and cousins ate copiously and solemnly at the Dinner, and afterwards, replete, went out for walks, their stomachs burning within, and their skin tingling without, exercising themselves gloomily in the icy rain, with the prospect of having to find room in an hour or two for heavy Christmas cake and mince pies. It was on occasions like these that the hatchets they had so carefully tried to bury became disinterred. They no doubt longed for the happy day on which they would be released from their filial duties, and would be allowed to return to their respective homes, there to pursue their internecine feuds undisturbed for the rest of the year.

L. STENI, 1901–

MEMORIES II

CHRISTMAS morning was always over before you could say Jack Frost. And look! suddenly the pudding was burning! Bang

138

the gong and call the fire brigade and the book-loving firemen! Someone found the silver threepenny-bit with a currant on it; and the someone was always Uncle Arnold. The motto in my cracker read :

Let's all have fun this Christmas Day,
Let's play and sing and shout hooray!

and the grown-ups turned their eyes towards the ceiling, and Auntie Bessie, who had already been frightened, twice, by a clockwork mouse, whimpered at the sideboard and had some elderberry wine. And someone put a glass bowl full of nuts on the littered table, and my uncle said, as he said once every year : 'I've got a shoe-nut here. Fetch me a shoe-horn to open it, boy.'

And dinner was ended.

And I remember that on the afternoon of Christmas Day, when the others sat around the fire and told each other that this was nothing, no, nothing, to the great snowbound and turkey-proud yule-log-crackling holly-berry-bedizined and kissing-under-the-mistletoe Christmas when *they* were children, I would go out, school-capped and gloved and mufflered, with my bright new boots squeaking, into the white world on to the seaward hill, to call on Jim and Dan and Jack and to walk with them through the silent snowscape of our town.

We went padding through the streets, leaving huge deep foot-prints in the snow, on the hidden pavements.

'I bet people'll think there's been hippoes.'

'What would you do if you saw a hippo coming down Terrace Road?'

'I'd go like this, bang! I'd throw him over the railings and roll him down the hill and then I'd tickle him under the ear and he'd wag his tail. . . .'

'What would you do if you saw *two* hippoes . . . ?'

Iron-flanked and bellowing he-hippoes clanked and blundered and battered through the scudding snow towards us as we passed by Mr Daniel's house.

'Let's post Mr Daniel a snowball through his letter-box.'

'Let's write things in the snow.'

'Let's write "Mr Daniel looks like a spaniel" all over his lawn.'

'Look,' Jack said, 'I'm eating snow-pie.'

'What's it taste like?'

'Like snow-pie,' Jack said.

Or we walked on the white shore.

139

'Can the fishes see it's snowing?'

'They think it's the sky falling down.'

The silent one-clouded heavens drifted on to the sea.

'All the old dogs have gone.'

Dogs of a hundred mingled makes yapped in the summer at the sea-rim and yelped at the trespassing mountains of the waves.

'I bet St Bernards would like it now.'

And we were snowblind travellers lost on the north hills, and the great dewlapped dogs, with brandy-flasks round their necks, ambled and shambled up to us, baying 'Excelsior.'

We returned home through the desolate poor sea-facing streets where only a few children fumbled with bare red fingers in the thick wheel-rutted snow and cat-called after us, their voices fading away, as we trudged uphill, into the cries of the dock-birds and the hooters of ships out in the white and whirling bay.

Bring out the tall tales now that we told by the fire as we roasted chestnuts and the gaslight bubbled low. Ghosts with their heads under their arms trailed their chains and said 'whooo' like owls in the long nights when I dared not look over my shoulder; wild beasts lurked in the cubby-hole under the stairs where the gas-meter ticked. 'Once upon a time,' Jim said, 'there were three boys, just like us, who got lost in the dark in the snow, near Bethesda Chapel, and this is what happened to them. . . .' It was the most dreadful happening I had ever heard.

And I remember that we went singing carols once, a night or two before Christmas Eve, when there wasn't the shaving of a moon to light the secret, white-flying streets. At the end of a long road was a drive that led to a large house, and we stumbled up the darkness of the drive that night, each one of us afraid, each one holding a stone in his hand in case, and all of us too brave to say a word. The wind made through the drive-trees noises as of old and unpleasant and maybe web-footed men wheezing in caves. We reached the black bulk of the house.

'What shall we give them?' Dan whispered.

' "Hark the Herald"? "Christmas comes but Once a Year"?'

'No,' Jack said: 'We'll sing "Good King Wenceslas." I'll count three.'

One, two, three, and we began to sing, our voices high and seemingly distant in the snow-felted darkness round the house that was occupied by nobody we knew. We stood close together, near the dark door.

Good King Wenceslas looked out
On the Feast of Stephen.

And then a small, dry voice, like the voice of someone who has not spoken for a long time, suddenly joined our singing: a small, dry voice from the other side of the door: a small, dry voice through the keyhole. And when we stopped running we were outside *our* house; the front room was lovely and bright; the gramophone was playing; we saw the red and white balloons hanging from the gas-bracket; uncles and aunts sat by the fire; I thought I smelt our supper being fried in the kitchen. Everything was good again, and Christmas shone through all the familiar town.

'Perhaps it was a ghost,' Jim said.

'Perhaps it was trolls,' Dan said, who was always reading.

'Let's go in and see if there's any jelly left,' Jack said. And we did that.

DYLAN THOMAS, 1914–53

MAHERSHALLALASHBAZ TUCK

December 25th, 1867: Married a young parishioner of the name of Mahershallalashbaz Tuck. He accounted for the possession of so extraordinary a name thus: his father wished to call him by the shortest name in the Bible, and for that purpose selected Uz. But, the clergyman making some demur, that father said in pique, 'Well, if he cannot have the shortest he shall have the longest.'

B. J. ARMSTRONG, 1817–90

DECEMBER 25th, 1870

A S I lay awake praying in the early morning I thought I heard a sound of distant bells. It was an intense frost. I sat down in my bath upon a sheet of thick ice which broke in the middle into large pieces whilst sharp points and jagged edges stuck all round

the sides of the tub like *chevaux de frise,* not particularly com-
forting to the naked thighs and loins, for the keen ice cut like
broken glass. The ice water stung and scorched like fire. I had to
collect the floating pieces of ice and pile them on a chair before
I could use the sponge and then I had to thaw the sponge in my
hands for it was a mass of ice. The morning was most brilliant.
Walked to the Sunday School with Gibbins and the road
sparkled with millions of rainbows, the seven colours gleaming
in every glittering point of hoar frost. The Church was very cold
in spite of two roaring stove fires. Mr. V. preached and went to
Bettws.   FRANCIS KILVERT, 1840–79

CHRISTMAS DAY
The Family Sitting

In the days of Cæsar Augustus
    There went forth this decree:
Si quis rectus et justus
    Liveth in Galilee,
Let him go up to Jereusalem
    And pay his scot to me.

There are passed one after the other
    Christmases fifty-three,
Since I sat here with my mother
    And heard the great decree:
How they went up to Jereusalem
    Out of Galilee.

They have passed one after the other;
    Father and mother died,
Brother and sister and brother

142

Taken and sanctified.
I am left alone in the sitting
    With none to sit beside.

On the fly-leaves of these old prayer-books
    The childish writings fade,
Which show that once they were the books
    In the days when prayer was made
For other kings and princesses,
    William and Adelaide.

The pillars are twisted with holly,
    And the font is wreathed with yew;
Christ forgive me for folly,
    Youth's lapses—not a few,
For the hardness of my middle life,
    For age's fretful view.

Cotton-wool letters on scarlet,
    All the ancient lore,
Tell how the chieftains starlit
    To Bethlehem came to adore;
To hail Him King in the manger,
    Wonderful, Counsellor.

The bells ring out in the steeple
    The gladness of erstwhile,
And the children of other people
    Are walking up the aisle;
They brush my elbow in passing,
    Some turn to give me a smile.

Is the almond-blossom bitter?
    Is the grasshopper heavy to bear?
Christ make me happier, fitter
    To go to my own over there:
Jereusalem the Golden,
    What bliss beyond compare!

My Lord, where I have offended
    Do Thou forgive it me,
That so, when all being ended,
    I hear Thy last decree,
I may go up to Jereusalem
    Out of Galilee.

J. MEADE FALKNER, 1858–1932

ON THE ATLANTIC

A T last the anchor was up, the sails were set, and off we glided. It was a short, cold Christmas; and as the short northern day merged into night, we found ourselves almost broad upon the wintry ocean, whose freezing spray cased us in ice, as in polished armour. The long rows of teeth on the bulwarks glistened in the moonlight; and like the white ivory tusks of some huge elephant, vast curving icicles depended from the bows.

Lank Bildad, as pilot, headed the first watch, and ever and anon, as the old craft deep dived into the green seas, and sent the shivering frost all over her, and the winds howled, and the cordage rang, his steady notes were heard—

> 'Sweet fields beyond the swelling flood,
> Stand dressed in living green.
> So to the Jews old Canaan stood,
> While Jordan rolled between.'

Never did those sweet words sound more sweetly to me than then. They were full of hope and fruition. Spite of this frigid winter night in the boisterous Atlantic, spite of my wet feet and wetter jacket, there was yet, it then seemed to me, many a pleasant haven in store; and meads and glades so eternally vernal, that the grass shot up by the spring, untrodden, unwilted, remains at midsummer.

HERMAN MELVILLE, 1819–91

COOKS AT SEA

T H E most disagreeable thing at sea is the cookery; for there is not, properly speaking, any professed cook on board. The worst sailor is generally chosen for that purpose. Hence comes the proverb, used among the English sailors, that 'God sends meat, and the Devil sends cooks.'

BENJAMIN FRANKLIN, 1706–90

PEACE

My soul, there is a country
    Far beyond the stars,
Where stands a winged sentry
    All skilful in the wars :
There, above noise and danger,
    Sweet Peace sits, crown'd with smiles,
And One born in a manger
    Commands the beauteous files.
He is thy gracious Friend,
    And—O my soul, awake!—

Did in pure love descend
    To die here for thy sake.
If thou can get but thither,
    There grows the flower of Peace,
The Rose that cannot wither,
    Thy fortress, and thy ease.
Leave then thy foolish ranges;
    For none can thee secure
But One who never changes—
    Thy God, thy life, thy cure.

HENRY VAUGHAN, 1622–95

LETTER TO TOM MOORE: XMAS 1820

Ravenna, Dec. 25.

Y O U will or ought to have received the packet and letters which
I remitted to your address a fortnight ago (or it may be more
days), and I shall be glad of an answer, as, in these times and
places, packets per post are in some risk of not reaching their
destination.

I have been thinking of a project for you and me, in case we
both get to London again, which (if a Neapolitan war don't
suscitate) may be calculated as possible for one of us about the

K

spring of 1821. I presume that you, too, will be back by that time, or never; but on that you will give me some index. The project, then, is for you and me to set up jointly a *newspaper*— nothing more nor less—weekly, or so, with some improvement or modifications upon the plan of the present scoundrels, who degrade that department,—but a *newspaper,* which we will edit in due form, and, nevertheless, with some attention.

There must always be in it a piece of poesy from one or other of us *two,* leaving room, however, for such dilettanti rhymers as may be deemed worthy of appearing in the same column: but *this* must be a *sine qua non;* and also as much prose as we can compass. We will take an *office*—our names *not* announced, but suspected—and, by the blessing of Providence, give the age some new lights upon policy, poesy, biography, criticism, morality, theology, and all other *ism, ality,* and *ology* whatsoever.

Why, man, if we were to take to this in good earnest, your debts would be paid off in a twelvemonth, and, by dint of a little diligence and practice, I doubt not that we could distance the common-place blackguards who have so long disgraced common sense and the common reader. They have no merit but practice and impudence, both of which we may acquire; and, as for talent and culture, the devil's in't if such proofs as we have given of both can't furnish out something better than the 'funeral baked meats' which have coldly set forth the breakfast table of all Great Britain for so many years. Now, what think you? Let me know; and recollect that, if we take to such an enterprise, we must do so in good earnest. Here is a hint,—do you make it a plan. We will modify it into as literary and classical a concern as you please, only let us put out our powers upon it, and it will most likely succeed. But we must *live* in London, and I also, to bring it to bear, and *we must keep it a secret.*

As for the living in London, I would make that not difficult to you (if you would allow me), until we could see whether one means or other (the success of the plan, for instance) would not make it quite easy for you, as well as your family; and, in any case, we should have some fun, composing, correcting, supposing, inspecting, and supping together over our lucubrations. If you think this worth a thought, let me know, and I will begin to lay in a small literary capital of composition for the occasion.

Yours ever affectionately,

B.

P.S.—If you thought of a middle plan between a *Spectator* and a newspaper, why not?—only not on a *Sunday*. Not that Sunday is not an excellent day, but it is engaged already. We will call it the 'Tenda Rossa' [Red Tent], the name Tassoni gave an answer of his in a controversy, in allusion to the delicate hint of Timour the Lame, to his enemies, by a 'Tenda' of that colour, before he gave battle. Or we will call it *Gli*, or *I Carbonari*, if it so please you—or any other name full of 'pastime and prodigality,' which you may prefer. * * * Let me have an answer. I conclude poetically, with the bellman, 'A merry Christmas to you!'

LORD BYRON, 1788–1824

POEM TO FRANCES: XMAS, *1900*

Dearest : whatever others see
Herein, it is no mystery—
That I find all the world is good
Since you are all the world to me.

You will not blame my boastful hours,
It is not of such souls as yours
To spew the wrath of sorrow out
Upon the harmless grass and flowers.

Do you fight on for all the press,
Wise as you are, you cannot guess
How I shall flaunt before God's Knights
The triumph of my own princess.

Almost this day of the strange star
We know the bonfire old and far
The whence all the stars as sparks are blown
Piled up to warm us after war.

There when we spread our hands like wings,
And tell good tales of conquered things
The tale that I will tell of you
Shall clash the cups of all the Kings.

I swear it shall be mine alone
To tell your tale before the throne
To tell your tale beside the fire
Eternal. Here I tell my own.

G. K. CHESTERTON, 1874–1936

CAROL FOR HIS DARLING

Tonight the Christmas landscape of the skull
throngs brightly with white images of angels,
like parallel ropes of pearl, poised above spires,
surmounting towers, ascending and descending.

Streets, squares, and gardens of the tired heart's town
receive snow-wise the promise of this song
which shuttles its theme like a glinting row of beads
between the icy earth and the granite sky.

Christ, sing the voices like uplifted candles,
is born again in memory's dim manger,
warmed by the friendly incense of the oxen;
miraculous and immaculate as snow.

The unrejoicing heart has resurrection;
joy burns in the air like an incandescent star.

148

But this is a story for our private theatre :
outside, the night is dank and uninspired.

Down by the shore the wave repeats its secret
of banal worth to the uninterested sand,
and, here, the senile ash in the funeral fire
utters its grey disintegrating sigh.

Darling, accept these symbols of thanksgiving,
these blanched and shining signs of blessedness,
these jubilations of the lonely night-time,
these holly-rites of a happy imagination.

It was your love designed this festival,
your love I feel as an ether-weighted flake
which falls, like the shy white Christmas snow, in my heart,
stroking its dales with a tingling finger of peace.

DEREK STANFORD, 1918–

NEVER MORE CHRISTMAS

THE curtains were rose coloured china silk and as I pulled them
apart I saw the snow flakes flattening themselves against the storm
windows, like tiny snowballs thrown at us by someone who
wanted to hurt us or make fun of us.

'Turkey, cranberry sauce, mince pies and Christmas pudding,'
he said. 'I can eat the lot. I do wish Mom would make chestnut
stuffing the way I had it in Paris that time. Trouble is with Mom
she will insist on sticking to American cooking. She just can't get
it into her head that maybe Old World cooking can be good too.
Bring on the dishes and the platters and the dancing girls; it's
Christmas, by God! Gee, I do feel good today! Honey, I really
feel I could eat a whole turkey and trimmings today.'

Now that I had drawn the curtains the room looked cool and
clear, and the hypodermic syringe on the night table sparkled
with reflected light like a glass decoration on a Christmas tree.
The rose red carpet we had chosen together looked like a patch
of the sky at dawn or at sunset. We really had chosen very carefully the things we wanted to have round us. We wanted the

very best of everything; we wanted to enjoy life to the full and to surround ourselves with everything that was beautiful.

'Say, Honey,' he said, 'when the old Doc comes, ask him if I can have turkey and cranberry sauce today. I sure would like to get my teeth into some turkey and brown potatoes and mashed yellow turnips and some lemon yellow sherbet between courses. And since it seems Mom is doing the Christmas Dinner this year, I surely would like to taste some of those pickled peaches she prepares.'

'I certainly will ask Doc all that, Honey,' I said. 'When he comes, I'll ask him.'

There was a kind of noisy silence round us. Outside, the snow was falling, as it were on padded feet, and in the house, sounds drifted up from the kitchen and the nursery, quite normally but muted, softened and quietened because somebody was dying in the house.

'Old Doc told me I might die tonight or I might live for ever. Jees! Wouldn't it be something to die on Christmas night!'

He moved his young head on the pillow and looked at me in astonishment.

'Honey. *Nobody* ever died on Christmas Day, did they?'

His head turned back over on the pillow and I could tell by the lines that hooped his mouth that it had come on again. The terrible pain had come on again.

So I took the crystal toy, the Christmas tree toy, the hypodermic, and, pinching his flesh between my fingers, I daggered in the needle.

Pain, although it was Christmas Day, was hard to exorcise. The pain would keep coming on, coming in like an uninvited Christmas guest, annoying, wearying, tiring, agonising.

Quite unpardonable, this gate-crashing visitor. Unsnubbable, determined to hold the floor, to shut out everything else, to inundate everything, flood out all feeling, drown life in a swamp of pain.

He fell asleep at last and the room we had made together gathered us up comfortably. Towards evening, while he still slept, I looked out of the windows again as I drew the curtains together.

Snow flakes were still flattening themselves against the glass and covering the arms of the trees outside. It was not so cold now, and the snow flakes melted a little, looking like tears, or, spreading over the window panes in a fine mesh, they seemed almost like thistledown, or the fine linen shroud that covers a dead child.

MARION AGNEW, 1906–

THE FEAST OF STEPHEN

After the midnight unfolding of the White Rose
Under the windblown stars; after the heartsease,
A bloodstain on the altar-cloth, veiling the cup
Red for Stephen's martyrdom.

After the silver fanfares of the Angelic heralds
Crying a truce and comfort, after this
The edged stones, the blade more bitter than flame;
These too, gifts of the Incarnate.

After the birth, the sowing, the bleak memorial
Of death the Harvester; after the swaddling clothes
The sweat-stained garments, heavy with dust and destiny
Stacked at the feet of Saul.

KEVIN NICHOLS, 1929–

BOXING DAY, 1929

RODMELL : I find it almost incredibly soothing—a fortnight alone—almost impossible to let oneself have it. Relentlessly we have crushed visitors. We will be alone this once, we say; and really, it seems possible. Then Annie is to me very sympathetic. My bread bakes well. All is rather rapt, simple, quick, effective—except for my blundering on at *The Waves*. I write two pages of arrant nonsense, after straining; I write variations of every sentence; compromises; bad shots; possibilities; till my writing book is like a lunatic's dream. Then I trust to some inspiration on re-reading; and pencil them into some sense. Still I am not satisfied. I think there is something lacking. I sacrifice nothing to seemliness. I press to my centre. I don't care if it is all scratched out. And there is something there. I incline now to violent shots—at London—at talk—shouldering my way ruthlessly—and then, if nothing comes of it—anyhow I have examined the possibilities. But I wish I enjoyed it more. I don't have it in my head all day like the *Lighthouse* and *Orlando*.

VIRGINIA WOOLF, 1882–1941

CELESTIAL FRUIT

The stars are golden fruit upon a tree
All out of reach.

GEORGE ELIOT, 1819–80

CHRISTMAS-TREE FRUIT

I HAVE been looking on, this evening, at a merry company of children assembled round that pretty German toy, a Christmas Tree. The tree was planted in the middle of a great round table, and towered high above their heads. It was brilliantly lighted by a multitude of little tapers; and everywhere sparkled and glittered with bright objects. There were rosy-cheeked dolls, hiding behind the green leaves; and there were real watches (with movable hands, at least, and an endless capacity of being wound up) dangling from innumerable twigs; there were French-polished tables, chairs, bedsteads, wardrobes, eight-day clocks, and various other articles of domestic furniture (wonderfully made, in tin, at Wolverhampton), perched among the boughs, as if in preparation for some fairy housekeeping; there were jolly, broad-faced little men, much more agreeable in appearance than many real men—and no wonder, for their heads took off, and showed them to be full of sugar-plums; there were fiddles and drums; there were tambourines, books, work-boxes, paint-boxes, sweetmeat boxes, peep-show boxes, and all kinds of boxes; there were trinkets for the elder girls, far brighter than any grown-up gold and jewels; there were baskets and pincushions in all devices; there were guns, swords, and banners; there were witches standing in enchanted rings of pasteboard, to tell fortunes; there were teetotums, humming-tops, needle-cases, pen-wipers, smelling-bottles, conversation-cards, bouquet-holders; real fruit, made artificially dazzling with gold leaf; imitation apples, pears, and walnuts, crammed with surprises; in short, as a pretty child, before me, delightfully whispered to another pretty child, her bosom friend, 'There was everything, and more.' This motley collection of odd objects, clustering on the tree like magic fruit, and flashing back the bright looks directed towards it from every side—some of the diamond-eyes admiring it were hardly on a level with the table, and a few were languishing in timid wonder on the bosoms of pretty mothers, aunts, and nurses—made a lively realization of the fancies of childhood; and set me thinking how all the trees that grow and all the things that come into existence on the earth, have their wild adornments at that well-remembered time.

Being now at home again, and alone, the only person in the house awake, my thoughts are drawn back, by a fascination which I do not care to resist, to my own childhood. I begin to consider, what do we all remember best upon the branches of the Christmas Tree of our own young Christmas days, by which we climbed to real life.

Straight, in the middle of the room, cramped in the freedom of its growth by no encircling walls or soon-reached ceiling, a shadowy tree arises; and, looking up into the dreamy brightness of its top—for I observe in this tree the singular property that it appears to grow downward towards the earth—I look into my youngest Christmas recollections!

All toys at first, I find. Up yonder, among the green holly and red berries, is the Tumbler with his hands in his pockets, who wouldn't lie down, but whenever he was put upon the floor, persisted in rolling his fat body about, until he rolled himself still, and brought those lobster eyes of his to bear upon me—when I affected to laugh very much, but in my heart of hearts was extremely doubtful of him. Close beside him is that infernal snuff-box, out of which there sprang a demoniacal Counsellor in a black gown, with an obnoxious head of hair, and a red cloth mouth, wide open, who was not to be endured on any terms, but could not be put away either; for he used suddenly, in a highly magnified state, to fly out of Mammoth Snuff-boxes in dreams, when least expected. Nor is the frog with cobbler's wax on his tail, far off; for there was no knowing where he wouldn't jump; and when he flew over the candle, and came upon one's hand with that spotted back—red on a green ground—he was horrible. The card-board lady in a blue-silk skirt, who was stood up against the candlestick to dance, and whom I see on the same branch, was milder, and was beautiful; but I can't say as much for the larger card-board man, who used to be hung against the wall and pulled by a string; there was a sinister expression in that nose of his; and when he got his legs round his neck (which he very often did), he was ghastly, and not a creature to be alone with.

When did that dreadful Mask first look at me? Who put it on, and why was I so frightened that the sight of it is an era in my life? It is not a hideous visage in itself; it is even meant to be droll; why then were its solid features so intolerable? Surely not because it hid the wearer's face. An apron would have done as much; and though I should have preferred even the apron away, it would not have been absolutely insupportable, like the mask. Was it the immovability of the mask? The doll's face was immovable, but I was not afraid of *her*. Perhaps that fixed and set change coming over a real face, infused into my quickened heart some remote suggestion and dread of the universal change that is to come on every face, and make it still? Nothing reconciled me to it. No drummers, from whom proceeded a melancholy chirping on the turning of a handle; no regiment of soldiers, with a mute band, taken out of a box, and fitted, one by one, upon a stiff and lazy little set of lazy-tongs; no old woman, made of wires and a brown-paper composition, cutting up a pie for two small children; could give me a permanent comfort, for a long time. Nor was it any satisfaction to be shown the Mask, and see that it was made of paper, or to have it locked up and be assured that no one wore it. The mere recollection of that fixed face, the mere knowledge of its existence anywhere, was sufficient to awake me in the night all perspiration and horror, with, 'O I know it's coming! O the mask!'

I never wondered what the dear old donkey with the panniers —there he is! was made of, then! His hide was real to the touch, I recollect. And the great black horse with the round red spots all over him—the horse that I could even get upon—I never wondered what had brought him to that strange condition, or thought that such a horse was not commonly seen at Newmarket. The four horses of no colour, next to him, that went into the waggon of cheeses, and could be taken out and stabled under the piano, appear to have bits of fur-tippet for their tails, and other bits for their manes, and to stand on pegs instead of legs, but it was not so when they were brought home for a Christmas present. They were all right, then; neither was their harness unceremoniously nailed into their chests, as appears to be the case now. The tinkling works of the music-cart, I *did* find out, to be made of quill tooth-picks and wire; and I always thought that little tumbler in his shirt sleeves, perpetually swarming up one side of a wooden frame, and coming down, head foremost, on the other, rather a weak-minded person—though good-natured; but the Jacob's Ladder, next him, made of little squares of red wood, that went flapping and clattering over one another, each developing a different picture, and the whole enlivened by small bells, was a mighty marvel and a great delight. . . .

Upon the next branches of the tree, lower down, hard by the green roller and miniature gardening-tools, how thick the books begin to hang. Thin books, in themselves, at first, but many of them, and with deliciously smooth covers of bright red or green. What fat black letters to begin with! 'A was an archer, and shot at a frog.' Of course he was. He was an apple-pie also, and there he is! He was a good many things in his time, was A, and so were most of his friends, except X, who had so little versatility, that I never knew him to get beyond Xerxes or Xantippe—like Y, who was always confined to a Yacht or a Yew Tree; and Z condemned for ever to be a Zebra or a Zany. But, now, the very tree itself changes, and becomes a bean-stalk up which Jack climbed to the Giant's house! And now, those dreadfully interesting, double-headed giants, with their clubs over their shoulders, begin to stride along the boughs in a perfect throng, dragging knights and ladies home for dinner by the hair of their heads. And Jack—how noble, with his sword of sharpness, and his shoes of swiftness! Again those old meditations come upon me as I gaze up at him; and I debate within myself whether there was more than one Jack (which I am loth to believe possible), or only one genuine original admirable Jack, who achieved all the recorded exploits. . . .

Still, on the lower and maturer branches of the Tree, Christmas associations cluster thick. School-books shut up; Ovid and Virgil silenced; the Rule of Three, with its cool impertinent inquiries, long disposed of; Terence and Plautus acted no more, in an arena of huddled desks and forms, all chipped, and notched, and inked; cricket-bats, stumps, and balls, left higher up, with the smell of trodden grass and the softened noise of shouts in the evening air; the tree is still fresh, still gay. If I no more come home at Christmas time, there will be boys and girls (thank

Heaven!) while the World lasts; and they do! Yonder they dance and play upon the branches of my Tree, God bless them, merrily, and my heart dances and plays too!

CHARLES DICKENS, 1812–70

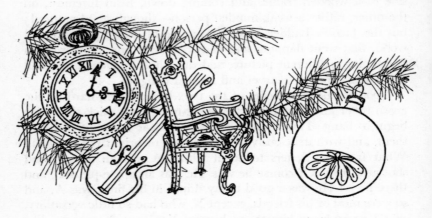

DICKENS THE DANCER

MR DICKENS led off the dance with Miss ——. I danced with Mr ——, Mrs —— with Mr ——. Let me tell you it was no fashionable ball-room dancing, such as walking through a quadrille; it was in the old style—we really danced! To see Mr Dickens with his legs in every direction (but they never seemed to touch the ground) capering about, enjoying it immensely, and appearing bursting with laughter [was a real amusement]; he has such a merry face. . . . We danced till our legs were nearly off, and we returned to the supper room, I escorted by Mr ——, where Mr Dickens made some stuff called 'Pip-Kin!'—which is hot whisky, set alight. We all laughed ready to expire. 'Now,' said he, 'we must Sir Roger. Mrs ——, may I have the pleasure?' I don't believe there was ever such a Sir Roger danced. We flew, we capered, we danced incessantly!—Mr Dickens stamping as he danced. . . . The order was always, 'Once more.' At last, however, it was over, and Mr Dickens (although it was two o'clock in the morning) sent us home in his own carriage. Was not this a real Christmas? He was as great a child as any of us. He knew how to spend Christmas.

AN AMERICAN YOUNG LADY, 1865

CHRISTMAS is pure delight, the climax of the year's festivals. Gunpowder in the smoky fog and the echoed pain darkened the November nights. The nights of December are never dark, but brilliant with the shine of Christmas, each day glowing more brightly until Christmas Eve, when everything bursts into a radiance that lasts over the pantomime on Boxing Day and dies fairly suddenly next morning.

Christmas food carries no unusual vernacular decoration; it is more special in kind than specially adorned. For instance, only a sprig of holly and burning brandy distinguish Christmas pudding from any other good one. The cake for Christmas tea has its own decoration though, being iced less formally than wedding or birthday ones, so that the icing looks rough like snow. A robin, a log and a spray of holly leaves (all edible) sit on the top and 'A Merry Xmas' is written across it. It has a frill of fringed scarlet paper tied with ribbon and more holly. Apart from this solitary cake, all the Christmas vernaculars are exotics, beautiful wooden boxes of muscatels, tangerines, crystallized fruit and Carlsbad plums.

The blown-glass ornaments on the Christmas-tree shine on the dark branches, like November's falling rockets hanging there. They are indeed crystallizations of all the fireworks, with tinsel for the silver rain and the white spun glass for sparklers. The commonest form, the basic decoration of every tree, is the plain sphere, one to three inches across, blown of the thinnest and most brittle glass (red, blue, or green, gold or silver). On this simple basis elaborate ornaments are built. The bauble may be painted in segments, or banded with circles of colour, have a rose on one side, or, most exciting of all, have one side recessed into a ribbed, glittering cave of gold or silver in a coloured ball.

At the very top of the trees is a golden tinsel star, and little twisted candles or electric lights burn in a metal clip at the end of each branch.

Above the tree, from corner to corner of the room festoon the paper chains. These are made of curiously cut pieces of coloured tissue paper glued into labyrinths. The chain comes from the shop folded flat. We attach it to one corner of the ceiling with a drawing-pin and pull it out across the room, a polychromatic concertina.

Paper also makes the crackers that we pull after Christmas

meals. The best kind of cracker is a cylinder of gold paper, lined with white, fringed at the ends and covered with cellophane in one of the seasonal, holly colours, ruby or emerald again. Between the cover and the lining runs the snap, two long strips of cardboard joined with a friction cap that explodes when pulled. The cracker is pinched into two neat little wasp waists and between them it holds a slip of paper with a motto and a very tight roll of coloured tissue paper in a band. This is opened out, and becomes a hat, fragile, rakish, creased and unbecoming. Costlier crackers contain novelties, jewels or indoor fireworks as well as hats, all tiny or closely folded. The crackers come in a big gaudy featherweight box : inside they are held in place with taut white thread in two flawless rows of six.

As well as parcelled presents in special holly wrappings, children get a lot of odds and ends enclosed in a large, rather shapeless net stocking, seamed up with red thread and tied with ribbons. It is beautifully arranged, with big and small, hard and soft, large box games and striped paper trumpets for substance, tin scales, boxes of chalks and sweets of mysterious consistency, like rubber marshmallow. The stocking, like the box of crackers and the tree decorations, weighs almost nothing; Christmas is a paradise of ephemera.

Boxing Day ends Christmas with a litter of screwed paper, a doleful aftermath at one with the deserted fair-ground and the winter arcade. The impermanence of the pretty decorations has set its canker on the year's end, a mood of cheap but uncomfortable melancholy.

BARBARA JONES

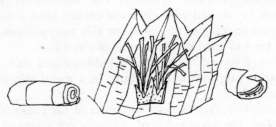

CHRISTMAS-BOXES

IN the very interesting collection of London Antiquities formed by Mr. Charles Roach Smith, and now in the British Museum, are specimens of 'Thrift-boxes; small and wide bottles with imitation stoppers, from three to four inches in height, of thin clay, the upper part covered with a green glaze. On the side is a slit for the introduction of money, of which they were intended as the depositories'; and as the small presents were collected at Christmas in these money-pots, they were called 'Christmas-boxes,' and thus gave name to the present itself. These pots were doubtless of early origin; for we find analogous objects of the Roman period. (See *Caylus, Recueil d'Antiquités*.)

In the *English Usurer,* 1634, the author, speaking of the usurer and swine, says:

> Both with the Christmas-boxe may well comply;
> It nothing yields till broke.

Humphrey Browne, in his *Map of the Microcosme,* 1642, says: 'A covetous wretch, he doth exceed in receiving, but is very deficient in giving; like the *Christmas earthen boxes* of the apprentices, apt to take in money, but he restores none till he be broken, like a potter's vessell, into many shares.' And in Mason's *Handful of Essaies,* 1621, we find: 'Like a swine, never good till his death; as *an apprentice's box of earth,* apt he is to take all, but to restore none till hee be broken.'—*Halliwell's edit.* vol. i.; quoted in Mr. Roach Smith's catalogue.

A gilt Nutmeg was formerly a common gift at Christmas, or festive times. Mars gives Hector 'a gilt nutmeg' in *Love's Labour's Lost.*

JOHN TIMBS, 1801–75

PURITAN PRESSURES

IN the afternoone came Col. Whaly, Goffe and others, from White-hall, to examine us one by one; some they committed to the Marshall, some to prison. When I came before them they took my name and abode, examin'd me why, contrarie to an ordinance made that none should observe any longer the Nativity (so esteem'd by them), I durst offend, and particularly be at Common Prayers, which they told me was but the masse in

English, and particularly pray for Charles Steuart, for which we had no Scripture. I told them we did not pray for Ch. Steuart, for which we had no scripture. I told them we did not pray for Ch. Steuart, but for all Christian Kings, Princes, and Governors. They replied, in so doing we praid for the K. of Spaine too, who was their enemie and a papist, with other frivolous and insnaring questions and much threatening; and finding no colour to detain me, they dismiss'd me with much pity for my ignorance. . . .

JOHN EVELYN, 1620–1706

PROVERBIAL TAILPIECE

After a Christmas comes a Lent.

JOHN RAY, 1627–1705

ACCURSED SEASON

ON the subject of all feasts of the Church my father held views of an almost grotesque peculiarity. He looked upon each of them as nugatory and worthless, but the keeping of Christmas appeared to him by far the most hateful, and nothing less than an act of idolatory. 'The very word is Popish,' he used to exclaim. 'Christ's Mass!' pursing up his lips with the gesture of one who tastes assafoetida by accident. Then he would adduce the antiquity of the so-called feast, adapted from horrible heathen rites, and itself a soiled relic of the abominable Yule-Tide. He would denounce the horrors of Christmas until it almost made me blush to look at a holly-berry.

. . . the year 1857 . . . saw a very strange sight. My Father had given strictest charge that no difference whatever was to be made in our meals on that [Christmas Day]; the dinner was to be neither more copious than usual nor less so. He was obeyed, but the servants, secretly rebellious, made a small plum-pudding for themselves. . . . Early in the afternoon, the maids . . . kindly remarked that 'the poor dear child ought to have a bit, anyhow,' and wheedled me into the kitchen, where I ate a slice of plum-pudding. Shortly I began to feel that pain inside me which in my frail state was inevitable, and my conscience smote me violently. At length I could bear my spiritual anguish no longer,

and bursting into the study I called out: 'Oh! Papa, Papa, I have eaten of flesh offered to idols!' It took some time, between my sobs, to explain what had happened. Then my Father said sternly: 'Where is the accursed thing?' I explained that as much as was left of it was still on the kitchen table. He took me by the hand, and ran with me into the midst of the startled servants, seized what remained of the pudding, and with the plate in one hand and me still tight in the other, ran till we reached the dust-heap, when he flung the idolatrous confectionery on to the middle of the ashes, and then raked it deep down into the mass.

EDMUND GOSSE, 1849–1928

'OH, FATHER, WHAT NONSENSE . . .'

I SAW all their nonsense at Christmas, and longed very much for Blanche and Toey to be in Rome to see the little Jesus which they stick up in most of the churches. In one church they had all the actors complete. First of all there was a model of a stable on a tolerably large scale, in which were placed two small models of oxen lying down quietly, while Our Saviour is represented by a small doll laying quietly in the Manger wrapped up in a little new hay. Close to the Manger stands the Virgin Mother looking very complacently at the little fellow, while Saint Joseph her husband stands opposite looking as if the child before him is a bastard. At a little distance stand the wise men from the east, and at a greater distance are the shepherds in their caves singing 'Oh be joyful.' Blanche and Toey would laugh at them, while Emily would say, 'Oh, Father, what nonsense.' Even poor, dear little George would, I think, laugh at the fun. In some of the churches the figures are made as large as life, but when this is the case there are only three of them, viz., Jesus, Mary and Joseph. The humbug practised on the poor deluded wretches here is horrifying. I have seen in Rome into the inside of one hundred and forty churches.

MR PAXTON, *fl.* 1880

L

MARGARET . . . felt the grotesque impact of the unseen upon the seen, and saw issuing from a forgotten manger at Bethlehem this torrent of coins and toys. Vulgarity reigned. . . . Margaret was no morbid idealist. She did not wish this spate of business and self-advertisement checked. It was only the occasion of it that struck her with amazement annually. How many of these vacillating shoppers and tired shop assistants realized that it was a divine event that drew them together? . . . 'No, I do not like Christmas on the whole,' she announced.

E. M. FORSTER, 1879–

PANTOMANIA

I OFTEN think with gratitude of the famous Mr. Nelson Lee—the author of I don't know how many hundred glorious pantomimes—walking by the summer wave at Margate, or Brighton perhaps, revolving in his mind the idea of some new gorgeous spectacle of faery, which the winter shall see complete. He is like Cook at midnight (*si parva licet*). He watches and thinks. He pounds the sparkling sugar of benevolence, the plums of fancy, the sweetmeats of fun, the figs of—well, the figs of fairy fiction, let us say, and pops the whole in the seething cauldron of Imagination, and at due season serves up the PANTOMIME.

Very few men in the course of nature can expect to see *all* the pantomimes in one season, but I hope to the end of my life I shall never forego reading about them in that delicious sheet of *The Times* which appears on the morning after Boxing Day. Perhaps reading is even better than seeing. The best way, I think, is to say you are ill, lie in bed, and have the paper for two hours, reading all the way down from Drury Lane to the Britannia at Hoxton.

W. M. THACKERAY, 1811–63

CHARITY IS SAGACIOUS

NOW for that other virtue, of Charity, without which Faith is a meer notion, and of no existence, I have ever endeavoured to nourish the merciful disposition and humane inclination I borrowed from my parents, and regulate it to the written and prescribed laws of Charity. And if I hold the true anatomy of my self, I am delineated and naturally framed to such a piece of virtue; for I am of a constitution so general, that it consorts and sympathiseth with all things. I have no antipathy, or rather idiosyncrasie, in dyet, humour, air, any thing. . . . I cannot start at the presence of a Serpent, Scorpion, Lizard, or Salamander: at the sight of a Toad or Viper, I find in me no desire to take up a stone to destroy them. I feel not in my self those common antipathies that I can discover in others: those national repugnances do not touch me, nor do I behold with prejudice the French, Italian, Spaniard, or Dutch: but where I find their actions in balance with my countrymen's, I honour, love, and embrace them in the same degree.

SIR THOMAS BROWNE, 1605–82

THE ELEPHANT MAN

A MORE burning ambition of Merrick's was to go to the theatre. It was a project very difficult to satisfy. A popular pantomime was then in progress at Drury Lane Theatre, but the problem was how so conspicuous [a human freak] as the Elephant Man could be got there, and how he was to see the performance without attracting the notice of the audience and causing a panic or, at least, an unpleasant diversion. The whole matter was most ingeniously carried through by that kindest of women and most able of actresses—Mrs. Kendal. She made the necessary arrangements with the lessee of the theatre. A box was obtained. Merrick was brought up in a carriage with drawn blinds and was allowed to make use of the royal entrance so as to reach the box by a private stair. I had begged three of the hospital sisters to don evening dress and to sit in the front row in order to 'dress' the box, on the one hand, and to form a screen for Merrick on the other. Merrick and I occupied the back of the box which was kept in shadow. All went well, and no one saw a figure, more monstrous than any on the stage, mount the staircase or cross the corridor.

One has often witnessed the unconstrained delight of a child at its first pantomime, but Merrick's rapture was much more intense as well as much more solemn. Here was a being with the brain of a man, the fancies of a youth and the imagination of a child. His attitude was not so much that of delight as of wonder and amazement. He was awed. He was enthralled. The spectacle left him speechless, so that if he were spoken to he took no heed. He often seemed to be panting for breath. I could not help comparing him with a man of his own age in the stalls. This satiated individual was bored to distraction, would look wearily at the stage from time to time and then yawn as if he had not slept for nights; while at the same time Merrick was thrilled by a vision that was almost beyond his comprehension. Merrick talked of this pantomime for weeks and weeks. To him, as to a child with the faculty of make-believe, everything was real; the palace was the home of kings, the princess was of royal blood, the fairies were as undoubted as the children in the street, while the dishes at the banquet were of unquestionable gold. He did not like to discuss it as a play but rather as a vision of some actual world. When this mood possessed him he would say: 'I wonder what the prince did after we left,' or 'Do you think that poor man is still in the dungeon?' and so on and so on.

The splendour and display impressed him, but, I think, the ladies of the ballet took a still greater hold upon his fancy. He did not like the ogres and the giants, while the funny men impressed him as irreverent. Having no experience as a boy of romping and ragging, of practical jokes or of 'larks,' he had little sympathy with the doings of the clown, but, I think (moved by some mischievous instinct in his subconscious mind), he was pleased when the policeman was smacked in the face, knocked down and generally rendered undignified.

SIR FREDERICK TREVES, 1853–1923

PANTOMIME PLAYED IN A CHARNEL HOUSE

I NOW come to one of the most curious incidents in my career. . . . Anxious to make a London reputation, I resolved, after consultation, to run a sort of winter theatrical show in conjunction with the conjuring.

So we took a large building in Clement's Lane, Strand, that has now been destroyed, the Law Courts standing on a portion of it.

This building, though very convenient for our purpose at the time, was one with a most unsavoury reputation. It was none other than the notorious Enon Chapel, erected as a speculation by a Non-conformist minister, who trusted to make it a paying one by taking advantage of the lax and insanitary conditions under which the dead were allowed to be disposed of prior to the passing of the Burial Act of 1850.

According to the facts given before the Committee of the House of Commons which was appointed to inquire into the system of London interments—facts that I may say I only learned later—Enon Chapel was registered for burials in 1823. From that date until the beginning of 1842, when the minister died, and the chapel after his interment in it was closed as a place of worship, over twelve thousand bodies were buried in the lower part of the chapel, only separated from the upper portion by a boarded floor. This space, in which the interments took place, was 60 feet by 30 feet and 6½ feet deep. Think of it, you who are blessed by the splendid sanitary arrangements of this age, and imagine what it meant in a crowded neighbourhood then, if you can!

Well, a few months after the chapel was closed it fell into the hands of other speculators. These worthies put a single brick floor over the old wooden one, another wooden one on top of the bricks, and then proceeded to make money by turning this charnel house into a low dancing-saloon.

There was no secret about the dancing being over the dead. That, in fact, was made one of the attractions, for an old bill, which well shows the character of the place and the kind of persons who used it, ran as follows:—

Enon Chapel.—Dancing on the Dead.—Admission three pence. No lady or gentleman admitted unless wearing shoes and stockings.

The scenes at Enon Chapel inspired some of Cruickshank's most biting caricatures, and at length, in 1848, a well-known surgeon of the day, a Mr. George Walker, purchased the place, in order to put an end to the scandal. At his own expense Mr. Walker entered into a contract with a builder to have all the bodies removed to Norwood Cemetery, and the floor properly bricked and cemented over. The cost was very great, for the men engaged in the gruesome work, which was done at night, had to be paid enormous wages; but the public-spirited surgeon saw the work through, and then allowed the place to pass out of his hands again.

It had been empty some months when I took it, in December, 1850. We played a round of pieces, gaff fashion, and for Christmas put on the pantomime, 'The Ice Witch, or Frozen Hard; or, Harlequin and the Mountain of Snow.' Being a fairly good operatic dancer, I played 'Patchy,' alias Harlequin, and Mrs. George Sanger skipped it on the light fantastic toe as Columbine. We gave five performances on Boxing Day, and engaged a band of twelve performers, who, in a wagonette drawn by two horses, used to play up and down the Strand and in other streets in the neighbourhood to advertise this unlicensed place of amusement.

Business was excellent, and we seemed likely to make a lot of money, when a sudden stop was put to our show. A police inspector who was an intimate friend of mine gave me a call and told me that it had been discovered that the contractor engaged by Mr. Walker had not fully carried out the terms made as to the removal of the bodies from Enon Chapel.

Some of his men had made known the fact that over a hundred barrels of human bones and remains, and, as a sort of grim joke, the coffin of the minister himself, instead of being removed, had been cemented up in the floor at one end of the building—in fact under the very spot over which my stage was erected.

The authorities, who were not favourably disposed towards gaffs, had resolved, as they were empowered to do under the new Burial Act, to raid and close the building until the remains were properly disposed of.

But the hint was sufficient for me without troubling the authorities. I was horrified to think that our pantomime had been carried on over the dead. I had heard much by this time of the awful history of the building, and resolved to clear out right away. So we stopped all the performances forthwith, dismissed our band, and removed all our properties and scenery to some large sheds in the Mile End Road.

'LORD' GEORGE SANGER, 1825–1911

T H E first time that Mercutio fell upon the English stage there fell with him a gay and hardly human figure; it fell, perhaps finally, for English drama. That manner of man—Arlecchino, or Harlequin—had outlived his playmates, Pantaleone, Brighella, Colombina, and the Clown. A little of Pantaleone survives in old Capulet, a little in the father of the Shrew, but the life of Mercutio in the one play, and of the subordinate Tranio in the other—both Harlequins—is less quickly spent, less easily put out, than the smouldering of the old man. Arlecchino frolics in and out of the tragedy and comedy of Shakespeare until he thus dies in his lightest, his brightest, his most vital shape, Mercutio.

Arlecchino, the tricksy and shifty spirit, the contriver, the busybody, the trusty rogue, the wonder-worker, the man in disguise, the mercurial one, lives on buoyantly in France to the age of Molière. He is officious and efficacious in the skin of Mascarille and Ergaste and Scapin; but he tends to be a lackey, with a reference rather to Antiquity and the Latin Comedy than to the Middle Ages, as on the English stage his mere memory survives differently to a later age in the person of 'Charles, his friend.' What convinces me that he virtually died with Mercutio is chiefly this—that this comrade of Romeo's lives so keenly as to be fully capable of the death that he takes at Tybalt's sword-point; he lived indeed, he dies indeed. Another thing that marks a close of a career of ages is his loss of his long customary good luck. Who ever heard of Arlecchino unfortunate before, at fault with his sword-play, overtaken by tragedy? His time had surely come. The gay companion was to bleed; Tybalt's sword had made a way. 'Twas not so deep as a well nor as wide as a church-door, but it served.

Ariel fulfils his office, and is not of one kind with those he serves. Is there a memory of Harlequin in that delicate figure? Something of the subservient immortality, of the light indignity proper to Pantaleone, Brighella, Arlecchino, Colombina, and the Clown hovers away from the stage when Ariel is released from the trouble of human things.

Immortality, did I say? It was immortality until Mercutio fell. And if some claim be made to it still because Harlequin has transformed so many scenes for the pleasure of so many thousand children since Mercutio died, I must reply that our modern Harlequin is no more than a marionette: he has returned whence he came. A man may play him, but he is—as he was first of all—a doll. From dollhood Arlecchino took life, and so promoted flitted through a thousand comedies, only to be again what he first was; save that as once a doll played the man, so now a man plays the doll. It is but a memory of Arlecchino that our children see, a poor statue or image endowed with mobility rather than with life.

With Mercutio vanished the light heart that had given to the serious ages of the world an hour's refuge from the unforgotten burden of responsible conscience; the light heart assumed, borrowed, made dramatically the spectator's own. We are not serious now, and no heart is quite light, even for an hour.

ALICE MEYNELL, 1847–1922

GILBERT AND SULLIVAN

I HAVE never seen Mr. Gilbert's clever play *Pinafore* performed by grown-up actors: as played by *children*, one passage in it was to me sad beyond words. It occurs when the captain utters the oath 'Damn me!' and forthwith a bevy of sweet innocent-looking girls sing, with bright happy looks, the chorus, 'He said "Damn me!" He said "Damn me!"' I cannot find words to convey to the reader the pain I felt in seeing these dear children taught to utter such words to amuse ears grown callous to their ghastly meaning. Put the two ideas side by side—Hell (no matter whether *you* believe it or not: millions do) and those pure young lips sporting with its horrors and then find what *fun* in it you can! How Mr. Gilbert could have stooped to write, or Sir Arthur Sullivan could have prostituted his noble art to set to music such vile trash, it passes my skill to understand.

LEWIS CARROLL, 1832–98

TRIALS OF AN AUTHOR

LEWIS CARROLL was fully prepared to miss the Christmas market rather than hurry an edition [through the press], and yet for all his care mistakes crept in. They became an obsession; he felt them as an old lady feels draughts. Uneven inking, cropped margins, irregular levels of opposite pages—he missed nothing. Genuinely faulty copies, with pages in the wrong order, found their way to him as they do to all authors, and it struck him as exceedingly odd that these defects had a habit of appearing in his specially bound copies. It was less surprising than he supposed. The binders were called upon to produce at the same time a large ordinary impression and fifty copies in red, twenty in blue, twenty in green, two in vellum, one with edges uncut, one with primrose edges, and one with a piece of mirror on the cover—and the binders' heads span. The publishers' also: 'Have you done any more with coloured inks and papers?' 'Have you ever considered the effect of *gold* type?' and when, in 1869, he produced his book of verses, *Phantasmagoria*, he wanted one edition, containing an Oxford squib, to be sold for 5s. 6d., and another, without it, for sixpence less.

CHARLES MORGAN, 1894–1958

IN RETROSPECT IN 1857

ALL mortals are tumbling about in a state of drunken saturnalia, delerium, or quasi-delerium, according to their several sorts; a very strange method of thanking God for sending them a Redeemer; a set singularly worth 'redeeming,' too, you would say. I spent Christmas and the two days following in grim contention all day each time with the most refactory set of proof-sheets . . . ; the sternly sad remembrance of another Christmas [when my mother died] present to me also at all moments, which made a strange combination, peculiarly tragic when I had time to see it from a distance, like a man set to whittle cherry-stones and toy boxes in the Valley of the Shadow of Death.

THOMAS CARLYLE, 1795–1881

THANKS FOR A PRESENT

(To Maurice Baring)

Of all the gifts of God by far
The best is Russian Caviare

HILAIRE BELLOC, 1870–1953

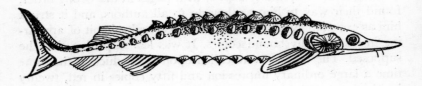

WHEN I WAS FIFTEEN

January 1st, 1904: It is twelve o'clock. All the bells in the village churches are pealing. Another year has come. Now, at the entrance of the New Year, my dearest, I propose to begin my book. It will not be at all regal or dramatic, but just all that I have done. You who are so far away know so little of what happens to me, and it is selfish of me not to tell you more. I have just returned from a midnight service. It was very, very beautiful and solemn. The air outside was cold and bracing, and the Night was a beautiful thing. Over all the woods and meadows Nature had tenderly flung a veil to protect from the frost, but the trees stood out, dark and beautiful against the clear starry sky. The church looked truly very fit for God's house tonight. It looked so strong, so hospitable, so invincible. It was only during the silent prayer that I made up my mind to write this. I mean this year to try and be a different person, and I wait at the end of this year to see how I have kept all the vows that I have made tonight. So much happens in a year. One may mean so well and do so little.

I am writing this by the light of a tiny peep of gas, and I have only got on a dressing gown. So *décolleté*. I am so tired I think I must go to bed. Tomorrow is the first of January. What a wonderful and what a lovely world this is! I thank God tonight that I *am*.

KATHERINE MANSFIELD, 1888–1923

I T is marvellous weather—brilliant sunshine on the snow, clear as summer, slightly golden sun, distance lit up. But it is immensely cold—everything frozen solid—milk, mustard, everything. Yesterday I went out for a real walk—I've had a cold and been in bed. I climbed with my niece to the bare top of the hills. Wonderful it is to see the footmarks on the snow—beautiful ropes of rabbit prints, trailing away over the brows; heavy hare marks; a fox, so sharp and dainty, going over the wall; birds with two feet that hop; very splendid straight advance of a pheasant; wood-pigeons that are clumsy and move in flocks; splendid little leaping marks of weasels, coming along like a necklace chain of berries; odd little filigree of the field-mice; the trail of a mole— it is astonishing what a world of wild creatures one feels round one, on the hills in the snow. From the height it is very beautiful. The upland is naked, white like silver, and moving far into the distance, strange and muscular, with gleams like skin. Only the wind surprises one, invisibly cold; the sun lies bright on a field, like the movement of a sleeper. It is strange how insignificant in all this life seems. Two men, tiny as dots, move from a farm on a snow slope, carrying hay to the beasts. Every moment they seem to melt like insignificant spots of dust; the sheer, living, muscular white of the uplands absorbs everything. Only there is a tiny clump of trees bare on the hill-top—small beeches— writhing like iron in the blue sky.—I wish one could cease to be a human being, and be a demon. . . .

D. H. LAWRENCE, 1885–1930

THE FIELD TO THE SNOW

Snow, my Fall of Mercy, I have troubles to confess.
I should be shouting up to God the kind of field I am,
A naked acre for the wolf, a grave-yard for the lamb.
Oh think before you cover all beneath a fathom of peace!

I never told the hooded crow my heart was black as he,
Or screamed my thistle hate aloud to scare the gulls to sea;
The river was my lover; in my hard, cold pride
I broke that spear of his that rankled, rankled in my side.

Snow my Fate, oh heavy Pardon, hesitate to fall!
Your freezing absolution you may keep, keep, keep
Until I bring the dead to life who labour in my soul;
There's beauty that we might betray beneath a boon of sleep.

LILIAN BOWES-LYON, 1895–

FLOWERS OF FROST

THE hoar powder changes even the beauty of the familiar trees
into something that never becomes a matter of course. The
beeches that were yesterday a brood of giantesses are now insub-
stantial and as delicate as flowers of grass. The frost has been
heavy, and the fields between the road and the woods are pure
white without a seam. No footmark has touched the solitude,
and it looks as if no one ever would cross it and enter the dark
wood that is guarded so fairly. Nowhere is this inviolate look
of the frosted woods more memorable than on the outskirts of
London when the lamps on an open road are still glimmering
and men are hurrying towards their trains. At the verge of the
wood the haggard grey and drab umbelliferous plants are flowering again with crystal flowers. Inside the wood the frost has
played at other mockeries. Each fragment of chalk is capped
with ice, usually resembling a tooth, which is sometimes more
than an inch long, and either perpendicular or slightly hooked
at the tapering tip. The earth under the beeches has almost been
covered by moss and ivy, and they have not been reached by the
frost; yet here and there in the wood there is a gleam in those
dark leaves as white as a dewy mushroom. Lying over the ivy
is what might be the distaff, hastily thrown aside, from which
the Fates were spinning the thread of some singularly fortunate
pure life—a distaff as it were bound round the middle with
whitest wool. The distaff is a rotten peeling branch of beech,
and the wool is a frost flower, such as may be found on any
frosty, still day and always attached to a branch like this. The

frost looks as if it had grown out of the dead wood; it is white and glossy, and curled like the under-wool which the shearer exposes on the belly of a sheep when he begins to shear it for the first time; but it is finer than any wool, and the threads, as much as three inches long, are all distinct as if combed. On some branches there are more than one, and of these one may be a large handful and another no bigger than the curl of a new-born child. Often the same stick will be singled out day after day for this exquisite attention from the frost.

Of a different kind is the beauty of the blades of ice that will occasionally be found attached to one side, not necessarily the under side, of every twig on every tree in the wood, and to every dead stem of dock and ragwort in the neglected fields above. These blades, having an even or a serrated edge and either as clear as glass or powdered with hoar frost, reach a breadth of an inch or more and almost the thickness of a sword. When it thaws they fall in rustling, jingling, glittering showers, and lie on the earth in fragments that soon melt together into mounds of a tender grey.

There is never any lack of colour in the woods of winter and the wooded hillsides; but frost is the discoverer of some of the most delicate harmonies. For example, the tender green, silvered green and willow grey of the juniper foliage, the white of melting frost, the harder white of the rime where the shadows of the bushes preserve it from the sun, and the other white which looks pale blue against the dark green of yew trees. And, again, in an old marl-pit against the side of a hill you will often meet the harmony of clear white frost, the grey or drab white of the fraying marl itself, the softer and darker cygnet colour of the old traveller's joy floating above and about the hazel bushes at the foot of the cliff, the grey mud of the cart-ruts, the still darker shades in the bark and the crisp fallen leaves of white-beam below, while perhaps a cloud will rise out of the blue sky above and add the white of sunlit marble, or the rose drift after dawn will be reflected in the whites beneath it, or the vapour from some warmer spot will float over and hang and swirl and spread banner-like among the beeches at the side. Another notable harmony is made by the seashore when the moors are dappled and the sands white with frost, the tall waves foam-crested, the sky milky blue and pierced only by the morning star. There is a harmony of colour and sound between the frost on the mountains and the curlew's cry. Beautiful are the rough ploughlands whose clods and ridges hold the frost and form a chequer which is repeated by the hard and almost rice-like clouds in the lofty sky.

Frost seems also to play a part in sharpening the characteristic odours of winter, such as the smell of cherrywood or the currant bushes freshly cut by the pruner, of tar when they are dipping hop-poles, the soil newly turned and the roots exposed by the gardeners. And there is a peculiar languid sweetness in the smell of grass when the rime is melting rapidly under the sun. Above all, the fragrance of the weed-fire is never so sweet as when its bluish and white smoke heaves and trails heavily and takes wing at dawn over the frost and its crimson reflections of the flames and among the yellow tassels of the dark hedge.

EDWARD THOMAS, 1878–1917

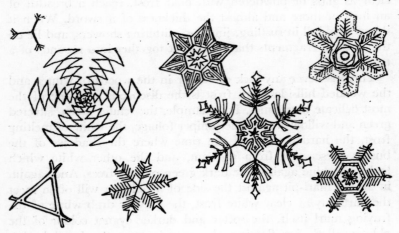

LIFE AFTER ALL

MABEL is very happy now—and it is like this : she has got over the terrible business of living and heartbreak, and has formed a circle, an entirely new circle, which she is quite certain will never let her down in the only too usual way that human beings have of doing.

She still lives as she has for the last thirty years in the big red brick block of flats, and has never even thought of moving anywhere smaller, or of shutting up any of the rooms. When she comes in from shopping, through the main entrance, and surveys

the magnificent width and height of the stony mausoleum, enlivened here and there by a brass potted plant, it is with something approaching real ecstasy that she mumbles to herself, 'Ah!
room enough for a carriage and pair to drive up.'

It has not always been like this. Five years ago a terrible
thing happened. Her daughter Celia, the sweet adorable simple-
ton who had reached the age of thirty without developing any
beastly habits, began to die. 'Nine months,' they told her, 'perhaps a year if she's lucky.' She must never be told, Mabel
thought. And she never was.

The appalling season of gestation for cancer began. Cancer is
caused by unhappiness. Who had said that? No one that Mabel
could readily recall, but then ideas must spring from somewhere.
She put it to Celia one day in a tea-shop at Brighton where they
had come for a day's blow by the sea: 'Are you a happy gal?
Are you enjoying Mummy's surprise?' The girl fixed her with
enormous blue eyes that were as vacant as the wonderful skies
over Gib that she had seen as a young married woman; then
an uneven smile had trembled for an instant on her slightly
drooping lower lip before she replied: 'Yes, Mummy darling,
I'm a very happy gal.' Mabel had been reassured to hear the
same rich timbre as her own, and know at least that there had
been no deterioration in the family voice.

Then there were the degrees of non-acceptance to be cleared.
The fight that began with visits to fanciful doctors who said they
were magicians, and magicians who tried to pass as doctors, and
from thence to the faith healers: 'If you have the faith of a
grain of mustard seed . . .' she would whisper to herself as she
trundled her thirty year old child in and out of taxis and hired
cars, sometimes far afield on remote branch lines to discover the
essence of eternal life.

Things began to happen. There were hormones to begin with,
male hormones that were injected twice a week. Celia grew bonny
in her ignorance, adding to her tall thin frame pads of flesh that
were as reassuringly pink as if she had been a convalescent. Her
voice too became stronger, dropping a tone, then another half
tone until it was undistinguishable on the telephone from the
voice of Edward, Mabel's only living brother. This new Celia
developed tendencies of leadership; in a bossy but childish way
she took over the reins of the house from the moment that Mabel
began to wilt after a bad attack of influenza. She graduated

from the complete dependence of the schoolroom to threatening adulthood. Every day she went out to the shops before twelve. She made an appointment to meet the Italian grocer's assistant at the local Odeon.

Mabel, when she was fully recovered, went back to the original specialist—the man who had in the first place passed sentence. 'Look,' she said, 'at the miraculous change in my daughter, and dare to tell me that this is not a cure.' Yet he smiled with the finality of the executioner who already holds the rope in his hand and said : 'This is only a development on the way,' and the way was stony; there might be several green pockets of false hopes before the end.

The months flew by. In July Mabel suddenly decided to spend the small remains of her loose capital on new clothes and expensive outings. They went to the big shops in Oxford Street and bought clothes in the summer sales for a winter that would never come.

'It cannot be possible.' Sometimes the daughter would hear this muttered phrase on her mother's lips when she was moving around the flat, disturbing the fine deposit of the night air with a pink feather brush. 'What can't be possible, Mum?' Mabel would hear this question in all its thick stupidity and saved ignorance; and then with the idiot propheticness that comes from true simplicity, the girl would add : 'Everything is possible if you really want it.'

Mabel remembered the words at Christmas time, when she was lying alone in her bedroom with the curtains drawn tight across the window, trying to cut herself off from the white tinkling Christmas morning that was passing up and down the street—strings of brilliant scooters and dogs on wheels on their way to Regent's Park.

I am a middle-aged woman, she thought, from whom everything has finally been taken away. There had been her husband Claud lying waxy and resigned under the strip of deep purple; AT REST embroidered by strangers across the area of his heart. But she had seen the terrible fight that he had finally lost and she knew that it was a lie.

Of Celia's last days she could not even bear to dwell. She had erected a heavy monument over the whole episode that concealed all distressing details and yet marked out the place; she saw it as a lump of stone in the middle of her life that she

176

would never be able to manipulate but only learn to accept.

About eight weeks before the end Celia had suddenly flopped : like a rosy rubber ball she had begun to go down as if the air had been let out. She lay quivering on the bed in pained surprise. 'I think I must have picked up a bug,' she told her mother one day after the doctor had been, 'nothing to worry about, Mum ; let's find something to amuse ourselves while I'm stuck in bed.' So the Canasta board was introduced, and the cards spread daily over the plump blue eiderdown ; they played for low stakes, piling their joint winnings into the child's christening mug 'so we can have another blow at Bournemouth when I'm on my feet again.'

Mabel rose and sank in a whirlpool of minute hopes and overwhelming doubts ; she rarely came to the surface. She heard her daughter on one occasion speaking on the telephone to a friend : 'I'm really worried about Mummy, she's so peculiar these days. No, there's nothing I know of to cause it unless some of her investments have gone phut and we're on the rocks.' Mabel wished then desperately to reassure any doubt in the girl's mind. She went out and instructed her stockbroker to sell up a block of very paying shares which she turned into three dark mink skins to twist round her daughter's neck. It was worth the madness and the risk to see the sharp little blue points of light that came alive in the milky translucence of her eyes. Celia lay gasping with pleasure against the soft mountain of pillows with the bright wet looking fur hanging down over the high collared neck of her childish flannel nightgown. She stroked and spoke to the stiff pointed snouts and looked into the glassy eyes ; she could not reconcile herself quite to the silk covered hook that was hidden directly under the poor flattened chin of the little animal. She had never once used it, but preferred to sling the tails over her shoulder.

That was her last really conscious pleasure it seemed to Mabel ; very soon after that she passed the first barriers of life, slipping into a coma from which she never again stirred. At the end she was tenacious, clinging to her moorings as long as it was physically possible, supping up the oxygen as it was doled out and rallying and sinking in quick alternation. Her mother stood there rigid at her own helplessness. She was not directly conscious of thinking anything, but it seemed that somewhere at the back of her mind a voice was shrieking, again and again, without any belief

177

or hope, 'Look upon a little child.' But it was too soon—or too late.

It was on the bus one afternoon going down Baker Street that she first heard the voice; quite distinctly, like pennies dropped into her mind, at the Portman Square stop, she heard it say: 'Look into the first window as the bus turns into Oxford Street and you will see that it is all in white.' She did not take much notice, in the way that she did not attempt to follow up this opening of a conversation and make a reply, but as the 13 bus came out of the narrow bottleneck of Orchard Street, her eyes turned instinctively to the left, and there, white as the St. Moritz ski run for beginners, the shop window gleamed with a display of sheets and towels. 'This could be,' she told herself when she got home, 'wishful thinking, or a trick of memory; after all the big shops do tend to have their White Sale in January.' She was not convinced, but mildly stirred. When it happened again, and at exactly the same spot, she was on her guard: 'You will see a figure in the first window in a dark red evening dress and a three-quarter mink cape.' Behind the plate glass the web-footed assistants were struggling with a half naked wax woman. She got off the bus and walked back the few paces to watch them as they straightened the stiff limbs and pinned into shape the loose flowing dress; then they went away. There was no mink cape. Wrong, she pounced as if she had scored a point. Wait! The word dropped over the edge of her mind, laughing, mocking a little at her assurance. On the return bus ride, the figure stood serene and waiting, as it were for a taxi that would never be hailed; on its shoulders there rested a nearly full length cape of the darkest Russian mink.

Now these occurrences, ordinary in themselves and completely insignificant, struck deep into a mind that was not disturbed by phantasy. Had she seen an angel with a thirty-foot wing-span flying across the sun, or a crown of stars on the ceiling of her drawing-room, she would have been more inclined to think that she was going out of her mind; as it was, the bread and butterness of the revelations reassured her. One saw what one could easily accept; faith was a very small grain compared to the enormity of visual convention. Mabel began to think seriously to herself, weighing up the reality and strangeness; there was no one to whom she could really confide, so unconsciously she formed a division within herself that needed to be both sceptical and completely convinced.

Celia, she thought, several evenings later, as she sat under the thick yellow light of the standard lamp running her eyes up and down the small black print of *The Times* 'hatch and match' as she called it, give me a sign, show yourself to me—in your new grey silk dress. She closed her eyes to create an illusion; as a stage managing precaution she dropped her heavy lids to bring about the division between herself and whatever it might be. When she opened her eyes, Celia was sitting in the chair opposite her smiling into the fire; she was wearing her grey silk dress. Mabel opened her mouth to speak but found that the process of thought transmission was quicker. As soon as the questions formed in her mind, so she received the answers in Ceila's voice: this then was to be the manner of communication. Settling back into the depth of her arm-chair, she closed her eyes for better concentration and found now that it was not even necessary to know of the visual presence in the room other than by acceptance.

I never knew, Celia told her, *I never knew that I was going to die, not until three days before the end when I went into that coma; by then I had already escaped the boundaries of my body. I hovered about the room and watched myself fighting for breath on the bed, I knew then that I could never get back.* Then she thanked her mother in an unemotional but human tone for the love and the care she had lavished on her—and the deception.

Things had begun. For a time Mabel lay bathed in a warm sweet torpor, sweating her relief and absorbing it again so that not one drop of it was lost. She was no longer alone most of the time, and because of this, she could savour the brief moments of complete isolation. She would have liked to have had snapshots and mementos to pore over by herself; she would have liked to have stopped someone in the street and told them of her discovery, someone with the lost dog expression in their hurt naked eyes who would then explain how they too had experienced a great sorrow. She wanted an audience and perhaps, too, disciples. Then it was, without any effort at all on her part, simply by letting her eyes wander over houses and people, that she first saw the notice, pasted and not peeling, on the inside of a ground floor window: PSYCHICAL SOCIETY. The sudden impact of these unfamiliar words clicked like the secret combination of a safe. The door flew open, and a whole new range of experiences was suddenly revealed to her.

She did not find it difficult to adapt herself to the group who lapped around her like grey woollen waves. The background and emotional range she found very similar to her own; it was like a small body of mothers who shared together the fragments of childish conversation, who wound back into their cocoons to extract the precise flavour and tone of the dear forgotten nursery days of their lost children. There was humour too. Sometimes one could not resist the mischievous humour of the little guides, who were mostly children.

Development and manifestation. Mabel went about the development of her mind, according to the rules set down; she looked and saw into the bright white supernatural future. The light concentrated and glowed like a beeswax candle in her high bulging forehead and the fine point of her long pale nose.

Often, now, she could see the bedraggled and bald headed figures who hovered uneasily behind the expectant figures who came to seances: 'There is a man standing beside you,' she told one woman, 'who asks you to remember the old brown dressing gown and fish on Friday. He has grey hair, thin on the top and a small straight scar over his left eyebrow.'

'It's Jim.' The cry of recognition was from the heart. The wan spectre became now as weak and distorted as a reflection in a moving puddle. The live voices round her head closed in sealing off the tiny aperture through which it had been possible for the apparition to seep; she was rocking with the motion of a ship and the voices were like a collection of inane chatterers heard through the webs of exhaustion after an attack of sea-sickness. She found the effort of public medium, although it came naturally to her, ultimately unrewarding as the acts of mercy expended by public benefactresses on the unknown poor; but because of her capacity it became a duty. For days at a time she saw and interpreted the homely messages from the dear ones of strangers.

Celia was nearly always within calling distance. Her pale curly smile was in the loop or half circle of any broken circumference; it could start from the shallow lip of a tea-cup and build up from there. If it was an automatic means or crutch that Mabel imposed on herself to bring about what she wanted, she did not question it; she believed implicitly. She was glad too that she had never packed up the rows of dresses and coats that hung in their mothproof bags, for Celia had a way of always appearing in the right clothes for the day or season; she never made a mistake. Sometimes when she was really alone, Mabel would feel her way hungrily through the soft and gritty textures of the wools and silks, stroking lastly the empty pelts of the little rats who had given so much pleasure. Secretly she hoped they would wear out; she had not yet had the courage to go again to the 'Young Set' department and buy anything new.

Lately, there were other people in the flat, and over them she could not yet say that she was really pleased. It was in a way like being landed with evacuees who had to be tolerated in spite of herself. There was the woman with the coil of black hair who was always peering out of the window. Mabel had not yet spoken to her, but she supposed she would have to sooner or later. When Christmas came round she would certainly have to. The Prescotts were different. They were older, and further back; sometimes they appeared as misty and faded as the little strips of Victorian wallpaper that still remained at the back of the cupboards on either side of the chimney breast. She imagined that they would have been the first inhabitants of the flat when the block had been built in 1870. They did not move about much, but this was to be expected; they were oldish people—strangely out of time in their stiff winged collars and padded bell shaped skirts. The Prescotts were unassuming shadows who would need coaxing. Mabel liked the Prescotts because they reminded her of Great Granny and Grandpa who had died when she was three; she respected them, and thought they might grow fond of Celia.

Sitting by the fire one afternoon, quite alone, for Celia had not yet appeared, she thought about the winter months ahead; she could not continue for ever going to the Society each day, she was getting too old, and besides mixing with people she had never met became an increasing strain. I have my family and friends to consider, she excused herself. I will tell them at Christmas that I may have to drop out. Then she closed her eyes in the warm comfort of sustained security; happily she let it lap over her as she began to plan the party she would give for Celia. There was poor little Miss Mitchell who was really beginning to come out of her shell and, of course, the Prescotts! She would try to get round to asking the entire Prescott family—if she could get them.

ISOBEL ENGLISH, 1923–

POEM FOR THE EPIPHANY OF OUR LORD

Reges Tharsis et insulae munera offerent

I bring you gifts, Jesus, of praise,
much laughter and a child's desire,
sweet, tempered limbs and weakling ways,
frozen in chastity and bound in fire.

I bring you gifts, Jesus, of pain,
a price to pay and hurts to hide,
and tears a few till you again
resolve in joy your suffering-tide.

I bring you music and the strain
of far-off islands : see my hands
well taught to harmony and fain
to pipe celestial sarabands.

I bring you silence and the care
of lips not opened, and restraint
of eyes : I bring you shaven hair
obedient hands, the girdle of a saint.

I bring you earth and Adam's sin,
and the long folds of a Virgin's gown ;
new life, new love, and will to win
in victory an unpassing crown.

I bring you ALL held in Creation's span,
I bring you nothing, for I bring you MAN.

MICHAEL FENWICK, 1921–41

AN EPIPHANY RESOLUTION, 1663

January 6th (Twelfth Day) : This morning I began a practice,
which I find, by the ease I do it with, that I shall continue, it
saving me money and time ; that is, to trimme myself with a
razer : which pleases me mightily.

SAMUEL PEPYS, 1633–1703

THE ROBIN

T H E household bird, with the red stomacher.

JOHN DONNE, 1573–1631

REDBREAST TUNE

The robin is the one
That speechless from her nest
Submits that home and certainty
And sanctity are best.

EMILY DICKINSON, 1830–86

ROBYNS AND STARRES

W H E N *Theseus* was puzled and entangled in *Minos* Labyrynth, he found the twist of *Ariadne* to deliver him thence. The little Bird with the red breast, which for his great familiaritie with men they call a *Robyn,* if he meet anie one in the woods to go astray, and to wander he knowes not wither, out of his way, of common charitie wil take upon him, to guide him, at least out of the wood, if he wil but follow him; as some think. This I am sure of, it is a comfortable and sweet companion, in such a case. It is the manner in all countries likely, in doubtful wayes especially, where they seem to crosse one another, to set up pillars with hands, directing and pointing this way or that way; and you will not beleeve, what comfort it affordes to wearies Pilgrims, whose everie step out of their right way, is a greevous corrasive to them. The Kings had a *Starre,* as companion in their pilgrimage, to the Crib. And the Pastours of the Church, are so manie

Starres, to lead their Sheep, and to guide their subjects in the pilgrimage of their owne salvation. When the havens are crooked and perilous to passe to and fro, the publick care of common safeties, in the night especially, provides some burning torch or other, upon some turret-top, to admonish the Marriners, where they are, and fairly to guide and direct them into the wished port. This same provisioun hath the Wisedome likewise of the great *Creator* found out, to comfort and direct us, no lesse, in the open Seas, exposing a certain *Starre* among the rest, as a sure and infallible *Pharus*: But more truly and abundantly faire, in ordaining the Incomparable Virgin *Marie,* his blessed *Mother* to be our *Starre* in the dangerous and tempestuous Sea of the world; and therefore is heer very truly sayd in the Motto: *In Itinere Pharus.*   HENRY HAWKINS, 1571–1646

THE STAR-LED WISARDS HASTE . . . .

See how from far upon the eastern road
The star-led wisards haste with odours sweet . . .

JOHN MILTON, 1608–74

A FOOTNOTE

WE only get part of a poet's mind if we miss his philology; and Milton by his spelling reminds us that the Three from the East were both wise men and Magi.

JOHN FREEMAN

GOLD, FRANKINCENSE AND MYRRH

SOVEREIGNTY, sacrifice, and true burial rights—here lay the key to the gifts of the three wise men. For they were gifts before they were treasures; they were gifts before they became symbols; they were gifts intended as offerings such as the shepherds had first brought to the Child.   I. ANTHONY, 1900–49

THE THREE KINGS

Three Kings came riding from far away,
  Melchior and Gaspar and Baltasar;
Three Wise Men out of the East were they,
And they travelled by night and they slept by day,
  For their guide was a beautiful, wonderful star.

The star was so beautiful, large, and clear,
  That all the other stars of the sky
Became a white mist in the atmosphere.
And by this they knew that the coming was near
  Of the Prince foretold in the prophecy.

Three caskets they bore on their saddle-brows,
  Three caskets of gold with golden keys;
Their robes were of crimson silk with rows
Of bells and pomegranates and furbelows,
  Their turbans like blossoming almond-trees.

And so the Three Kings rode into the West,
  Through the dusk of night over hills and dells,
And sometimes they nodded with beard on breast,
And sometimes talked, as they paused to rest,
  With the people they met at the wayside wells.

'Of the child that is born,' said Baltasar,
  'Good people, I pray you, tell us the news;
For we in the East have seen the star,
And have ridden fast, and have ridden far,
  To find and worship the King of the Jews.'

And the people answered, 'You ask in vain;
  We know of no king but Herod the Great!'
They thought the Wise Men were men insane,
As they spurred their horses across the plain,
  Like riders in haste who cannot wait.

And when they came to Jereusalem,
  Herod the Great, who had heard this thing,
Sent for the Wise Men and questioned them;
And said, 'Go down unto Bethlehem,
  And bring me tidings of this new king.'

So they rode away; and the star stood still,
    The only one in the grey of morn;
Yes, it stopped, it stood still of its own free will,
Right over Bethlehem on the hill,
    The city of David where Christ was born.

And the Three Kings rode through the gate and the guard,
    Through the silent street, till their horses turned
And neighed as they entered the great inn-yard;
But the windows were closed, and the doors were barred,
    And only a light in the stable burned.

And cradled there in the scented hay,
    In the air made sweet by the breath of kine
The little child in the manger lay,
The Child that would be King one day
    Of a kingdom not human but divine.

His mother, Mary of Nazareth,
    Sat watching beside his place of rest,
Watching the even flow of his breath,
For the joy of life and the terror of death
    Were mingled together in her breast.

They laid their offerings at his feet:
    The gold was their tribute to a King,
The frankincense, with its odour sweet,
Was for the Priest, the Paraclete,
    The myrrh for the body's burying.

And the mother wondered and bowed her head,
And sat as still as a statue of stone;
Her heart was troubled yet comforted,
Remembering what the Angel had said,
Of an endless reign and of David's throne.

Then the Kings rode out of the city gate,
With a clatter of hoofs in proud array;
But they went not back to Herod the Great,
For they knew his malice and feared his hate,
And returned to their homes by another way.

H. W. LONGFELLOW, 1807–82

WINE AND GIFTS

See where the goblet of red wine is held,
One sentence from the star of Bethlehem spelled
In all the night's mysterious harmony.
Now the circle is restored,
Father, mother, infant Lord,
Whose light is veiled and secret like the sea.

And these who come from distant lands through drifts,
These Eastern men, the Magi with their gifts,
Give them refreshment, rest, and let this wine,
Interpreting those devious ways
Which led them to this hour of praise,
Show each predestined and his gift divine.

For none who enters this poor shed can err,
And the laid gifts, gold, frankincense and myrrh,
Under the rafters and the heavy trestles
Await, like garments not yet worn,
The body of the newly born
Whose life is imaged in the holy vessels.

Nor is there sword so secret but this wine
Can with its glittering weight and power divine
See its designs unsheathed. They did expect
The sword of Herod so to fall
On Him who in this ox's stall
Wakes into life and gives the night effect.

Hark how the angels sing while He sleeps on.
The snow is broken where their feet have gone
Who now are kneeling by the babe they see.

Though dark and thick is that foot-trace,
The wine and gifts reflect His face
Who makes this darkness brilliant as a tree.

VERNON WATKINS, 1906–

THREE GIPSIES

Three gipsies stood at my drifted door,
One was rich and one was poor
And one had the face of a blackamoor.

Out of the murdering moor they came,
One was leaping, two were lame,
And each called out my naked name.

'Is there a baby that wants within
A penny of brass and a crown of tin
And a fire of spice for original sin?

'Hold him high at the window wide
That we may beg for him a Bride
From the circling star that swings outside.'

'Rise up, rise up, you gipsies three
Your baskets of willow and rush I see
And the third that is made of the Judas tree.

'No boy is born in my bed this day
Where the icicle fires her freezing ray,
For my love has risen and run away.

'So fare you well, Egyptians three,
Who bow and bring to me the key
From the cells of sin to set us free.'

Out of the million-angeled sky
As gold as the hairs of my head and thigh
I heard a new-born baby cry.

'Come back, come back, you gipsies three
And put your packs by my Christmas tree
For it is my son's nativity!'

Over the marble meadow and plain
The gipsies rode by the river's skein
And never more did they come again.

I set a star in the window tall,
The bread and wine in my waiting hall
And a heap of hay in the mangers all,

But the gipsies three with their gifts were gone,
And where the host of heaven had shone
The lunatic moon burned on, burned on.

CHARLES CAUSLEY, 1917

NOTES ON THE MAGIANS

THE wise men were Magians, either Zoroastrians or at least of
a religion or sect of philosophy (Sabaeism) in which astrology
played a part. And astrology is astronomy, ordinary science, with
an extraordinary science added. This is called after them *magic*
and there is therefore according to the Scripture a good or
'white' magic, lawful in itself though positively or from its
dangers it may be unlawful. That is, there is above all natural
science a science which bridges over the gulf between human
and superhuman knowledge, that is, enters a world of spirits, not
departed souls but angels. And therefore natural bodies like the
stars may exercise not only a natural, as by their light and
weight, but also a preternatural influence on man. That they
cannot determine his fate is plain from many reasons, among

which I now see that those which convinced St Austin and St Gregory are good. For a horoscope is a momentary cast or determination of the whole heaven, to which according to the ancients, and we may say in truth, the earth is like a point: in this enormous, infinite, disproportion only one thing is to be considered, the aspect of the place of birth, that is the relation between that and the heavenly sphere; this alone decides the horoscope, for all differences here below, *within* the same aspect, so long as they make no difference in the horoscope itself, can count for nothing, any more than difference of position between the men or houses make any sensible difference in the parallelism of their shadows in the sun. So then two men born within a few seconds or minutes of one another, too few to change the horoscope and in the same street, must have the same fate; which is not the case.

But that the stars might not determine a fate but influence a man's constitution and with it his history is not inconceivable. From their great distance this is either small or at least difficult to observe: astronomy succeeds with difficulty in measuring for instance the heat shed by Sirius upon the earth; his actinism may be more considerable: these are natural influences; it would seem that the Magians professed to observe preternatural, that is angelic, influences, and did so

The star was nothing to ordinary observers, perhaps not visible at all to them. For as in modern science most of the phenomena are known to astronomers, to the specialists, only; the public could scarcely remark if a star of the first magnitude were withdrawn from Orion; so still more with a secret art. So the Magi behave: nothing of *the star which appeared* or *how appeared*; it is *we have seen*; they speak of their art, their observation, magisterially. So that the star may have been an altogether preternatural appearance, only visible after the practice of their art, some sort of evocation, had been gone through, not necessarily always there; as in fact it disappeared.

If they were Persian Magians they may of course have come from Bactria and the borders of India. More reasonable to suppose the East because of its scriptural meaning, cf. Arabia east of the Holy Land. They were then of the Sabean, the very ancient religion of those parts, in them seemingly not idolatrous. *The King of the Jews* more natural to people of that country; also that they should be chiefs or kings than if they had been Persians

Date of coming uncertain. For the mystery one would suppose *after* the Circumcision, by which Christ, so to say, qualified as King *of the Jews*. Twelve days = 6 + 6 — Creation and Redemption, also a sort of mystical year, meaning the fulness of time. As a round number chosen for the feast one would rather have expected 14, octave of New Year's day or 10. It must have been before the Purification, as then probably the Holy Family would leave Bethlehem

Where is he etc. They know when, they ask where. Jerusalem troubled; their coming unwelcome, they knew more than the Jews, came to teach them. The Jews looked for the homage of the Gentiles: when it came it brought an unexpected circumstance with it, as God's works always do, the Gentiles the teachers, more honoured than themselves—though only in one particular

The Scribes called together secretly as far as possible, and the confirmation at least given secretly to the Wise Men. They go away by night, it may be by their own wish, to lose no time; but also by Herod's, that their going may be, unlike their coming, without noise. (Presumably night, for they see the star.) He sent them to Bethlehem, that is sent a guide to shew the road, courtesy so requiring. Writers ask why did he not send someone to report where they went. There could be a difficulty: it must be secretly, and from them. He could not commit himself by any known messenger; he would then seem to be recognising the Pretender. In the urgency he might not find a secret follower, and he thought there was no need. Then probably they do not enter Bethlehem. The stable was outside. The Bethlehemites saw little of them, did not know where they went. They would encamp near the spot and the dream was that very night; they set out before morning, and Herod altogether lost sight of them

Herod had meant to say on their return, that they were mistaken, this could not be the expected King etc., and afterwards to treat the matter as a conspiracy. No doubt he still more treated it so when he found himself 'mocked.' He probably does not act at once, but waits some weeks or months for a pretext, for the conspiracy to show itself. But the Bethlehemites had no plot and little knowledge on the subject. There was the story of the shepherds, but, so to say, nothing had followed it. After the Purification the Holy Family had probably disappeared. Herod of course availed himself of the registration and found St Joseph's name and place of abode and so marked out Christ for death; but not as a likely, rather as an unlikely, case. For by enquiring at Nazareth it would have appeared that the birth of Joseph's child at Bethlehem must have been a chance (and no doubt they had stayed at home till the last date possible), so that there could not well have been a plot. When Herod acted at last he must have pretended a conspiracy, required a confession, and getting none made this proof of general guilt, and so justified a general slaughter. The number of children killed cannot have been great, *a bimatu et infra*, that is probably from the beginning of the second year, one full year from birth.

The Magians had been clear about the star shewing the fact of the Christ's *being now* born, and born within a year: they did not know or they did not tell Herod it meant he was born at the hour of the star's appearance. Some of the children born within the year may have left Bethlehem; Herod would ascertain this and have them killed where found, but no doubt most were still at Bethlehem, and it would be a point with him to strike suddenly and once only, to give no alarm; he must then have meant the Nazareth murder to take place on the same day as the Bethlehem one. It was then the night before this day probably that St Joseph was warned and fled. When Herod heard this he must have then at last suspected this was the most dangerous of his rivals, and have been tortured by the thought till he died. He must have thought his agents had betrayed him too.

GERARD MANLEY HOPKINS, 1844–89

IN PRAISE OF THE CAMEL

With strength and patience all his grievous loads are borne,
And from the world's rose-bed he only asks a thorn.

WILLIAM R. ALGER, 1822–1905

DOWN WITH THE HOLLY, IVY, ALL . . .

i

Down with the rosemary, and so
Down with the bays and mistletoe;
Down with the holly, ivy, all
Wherewith ye dressed the Christmas Hall:
That so the superstitious find
No one least branch there left behind:
For look, how many leaves there be
Neglected, there (maids, trust to me)
So many Goblins you shall see.

ii

Kindle the Christmas brand, and then
   Till Sunset let it burn;
Which quench'd, then lay it up again
   Till Christmas next return.
Part must be kept wherewith to teend
   The Christmas log next year,
And where 'tis safely kept, the fiend
   Can do no mischief there.

iii

End now the white loaf and the pie,
And let all sport with Christmas die.

ROBERT HERRICK, 1591–1674

TIME WAITS FOR NONE

CHRISTMAS interposed its delays too, so that Twelfth Night
had come and gone before *Little Nell* died.

JOHN FORSTER, 1812–76

A HUNDRED NOT OUT

CHRISTMAS is not what it was! Such is the perennial cry at
Twelfth Night. The turkey, it is said, was tougher than usual;
the New Year balls were less exciting, the singing of the choir
feeble by previous comparisons. And thus it shall probably ever
be. For to capture the excitement of our youth we must wait for
our second childhood. In the meantime sorrows will have shaped
us, and memories from the past will crowd upon us until with
the accumulated wisdom of the years we may learn to say, 'the
Last was the Best Christmas.' However if we are very wise and
Epiphany Day has already been crossed off our calendars and
we are already thinking of Easter, and then of summer, we may
perhaps learn to realize that not only was the last the best but
that perhaps 'the Best is yet to Come.'

JAMES P. KENION, 1880–

THE MAGI DEPART

Now as at all times I can see in the mind's eye,
In their stiff, painted clothes, the pale unsatisfied ones
Appear and disappear in the blue depth of the sky
With all their ancient faces like rain-beaten stones,
And all their helms of silver hovering side by side,
And all their eyes still fixed, hoping to find once more,
Being by Calvary's turbulence unsatisfied,
The uncontrollable mystery on the bestial floor.

W. B. YEATS, 1865–1939

ACKNOWLEDGMENTS

I WISH to thank the following for their help in preparing this Christmas selection : Mr John Betjeman; Miss Dorothy Collins; Mrs Margerie Fenwick; Mr Jeoffrey Furbank; Mr Roland Gant; Mrs Grace Ginnis; the Mother Prioress, the Carmelite Convent, Presteigne; Miss Nesta de Robeck; Father Brocard Sewell, O. Carm.; Mr Derek Stanford; Mrs Helen Thomas; and Professor Carl J. Weber. I must here include as well Mr John Greaves, the Secretary of Dickens House, London; Miss Margaret Haferd, the Librarian at the American Embassy, London; Mr John R. McKenna, the Librarian at Colby College, Maine; and the Staff of the Reading Room at the British Museum. I am particularly indebted to Miss Barbara Jones for her drawings, and to Mr Lawford Siddall, the Headmaster of the Henry Fawcett School, London, for the time that he put at my disposal over the selection of the children's nativity paintings. I would like also to thank Mr Robin Denniston, Mr Michael Longman and Mr John McHale for their assistance during various stages of the book's progress.

For permission to include copyright material by W. H. Auden, I must acknowledge Messrs Faber & Faber Ltd and Messrs Random House Inc (*For the Time Being*); by J. W. Mackail, The Oxford University Press and Miss C. Mackail (*The Aeneid*); by W. F. Jackson Knight, Messrs Faber & Faber Ltd (*Roman Vergil*); by Elizabeth Hamilton, Messrs André Deutsch Ltd and Messrs Charles Scribner's Sons (*Put off Thy Shoes*); by Nesta de Robeck, Messrs Burns Oates Ltd and The Bruce Publishing Company (*The Story of the Christmas Crib*); by Andrew Young, Messrs Rupert Hart-Davis Ltd (*Collected Poems*); by Norman Douglas, Messrs Heinemann Ltd (*Venus in the Kitchen*); by David Daiches, Messrs Macmillan & Co Ltd and Messrs Harcourt, Brace & Co Inc (*Two Worlds*); by Patricia Hutchins, Messrs Methuen & Co Ltd (*James Joyce's World*); by Max Beerbohm, Messrs Heinemann Ltd (*A Christmas Garland*); by Arnold Bennet, Messrs Cassell & Co Ltd, The Viking Press Inc and the Estate of Arnold Bennet (*Journals*); by W. N. P. Barbellion, Messrs Chatto & Windus Ltd and Messrs Doubleday & Co Inc (*The Diary of a Disappointed Man*); by Thomas Hardy, Colby College Library, Waterville, Maine (*The Thieves Who Couldn't Help Sneezing*); by Henry James, Messrs Macmillan & Co Ltd and Messrs John Farquharson Ltd (*The Spoils of Poynton*); by Rupert Hart-Davis, Messrs Macmillan & Co

Ltd (*Hugh Walpole*); by Kenneth Grahame, Messrs Methuen & Co Ltd, Messrs Curtis Brown Ltd and Messrs Charles Scribner's Sons (*The Wind and the Willows*); by David Jones, Messrs Faber & Faber Ltd (*The Anathemata*); by Robert Lowell, Messrs Faber & Faber Ltd and Messrs Harcourt, Brace & Co Inc (*Poems, 1938–49* and *Lord Weary's Castle*); by Sandys Wason, the Editor of *The Cornish Review*; by T. S. Eliot, Messrs Faber & Faber Ltd and Messrs Harcourt, Brace & Co Inc (*Murder in the Cathedral*); by Roy Campbell, The Bodley Head Ltd and Mrs Mary Campbell (*Collected Poems*); by Dylan Thomas and Messrs J. M. Dent & Sons Ltd, the Estate of Dylan Thomas and Messrs Harold Ober Associates Inc (*Quite Early One Morning*); by Gertrude Bell, Messrs Ernest Benn Ltd (*Letters*); by B. J. Armstrong, Messrs George Harrap & Co Ltd (*A Norfolk Diary*); by Francis Kilvert, Messrs Jonathan Cape Ltd and Messrs Macmillan Co Inc (*Journals*); by G. K. Chesterton, Miss Dorothy Collins (unpublished mss.); by Derek Stanford, Messrs Routledge & Kegan Paul Ltd (*Music for Statues*); by Virginia Woolf, The Hogarth Press Ltd and Mr Leonard Woolf (*Journals*); by Barbara Jones, The Architectural Press Ltd (*The Unsophisticated Arts*); by E. M. Forster, Messrs Edward Arnold Ltd (*Howard's End*); by Sir Frederick Treves, Messrs Cassell & Co Ltd (*The Elephant Man*); by 'Lord' George Sanger, Messrs J. M. Dent & Sons Ltd (*Seventy Years a Showman*); by Alice Meynell, Messrs Burns Oates Ltd (*Essays*); by Charles Morgan, Messrs Macmillan & Co Ltd (*The House of Macmillan*); by Hilaire Belloc, Messrs Hollis & Carter Ltd (*Letters*); by Katherine Mansfield, The Society of Authors, London (*Journals*); by D. H. Lawrence, Messrs Heinemann Ltd, Messrs Laurence Pollinger Ltd and The Viking Press Inc (*Letters*); by Lilian Bowes-Lyon, Messrs Jonathan Cape Ltd (*Collected Poems*); by Edward Thomas, Mrs Helen Thomas and the Proprietors of *Country Life*; Gerard Manley Hopkins, The Oxford University Press (*Spiritual Sermons and Devotional Writings*); by W. B. Yeats, Messrs Macmillan & Co Ltd, Messrs A. P. Watt & Son and The Macmillan Co Inc (*Collected Poems*).